ABOUT THE AUTHORS

Simon Raven and Chris Raven were born in England in 1974. *Living the Linger* is their first novel.

www.samosirbooks.com

SIMON RAVEN   CHRIS RAVEN

Living the Linger

samosir
BOOKS

SAMOSIR BOOKS

Published by Samosir Books, United Kingdom
www.samosirbooks.com
First Published in Great Britain in 2005 by Samosir Books

Printed in Thailand.

A CIP catalogue record for this book is available from the
British Library.

ISBN 0-9548842-0-5

Cover artwork by Clara Pages, Buenos Aires, Argentina
Edited by Paul Raven

For David, Paul and Joan.

Contents

Club 747

Disturbed by the sight of an obese woman in tight yellow leggings reaching for her bag in the overhead locker, I turn and smile moronically at Chris.

'Are you OK?'

Deep in thought, or maybe just monged out, he ignores me and continues to stare into space.

Everything before now is a blur. I vaguely recall standing at the airport check-in desk, and tasting the worst cup of coffee of my life in some over-priced cafe. But I don't remember finding my way onto the flight or feeling any emotion as our trip begins. Scanning the compartment, I fail to recognise any of my fellow passengers from the gate. For all I know, Chris has switched our tickets and I would be none-the-wiser until our plane touches down in Azerbaijan. Leaning back in my seat I feel the plane tilt to the right, and from over the wing I watch London disappear behind a cloud.

'Chris! Are you all right?'

'Yeah, I'm fine.'

'What you thinking about?'

'Nothing, really. I was just trying to imagine what a jumbo jet would look like if you took out all the seats. It'd be *huge* wouldn't it?'

'Would it?'

He nods. 'If you gutted a 747, including the cargo hold, it would be absolutely massive. You could easily turn it into an exclusive nightclub or a trendy bar. I can see it now in flashing neon lights: *Club 747*. Don't you reckon?'

'Uh…'

'You could make upstairs the VIP lounge, put a DJ in the cockpit and split the downstairs into rooms playing different styles of music. It's a genius idea! All of the stars would go. In fact, why hasn't Richard Branson thought of it? We should write him a letter.'

Chris has always had an incredible fascination with planes. Not in a geeky way, a perverted one maybe, but ultimately he's just amazed by the simple fact that something so big can fly. As a grown man, I once caught him setting the video to record a TV show called *Big Stuff*. Each week a ridiculously over-enthusiastic presenter would visit buildings, machines or canyons of vast proportions, and use endless analogies to describe just how massive they really are. Chris lapped up this gigantic orgy of might, taping the whole series and gathering together enough wanking material to last him a lifetime.

It was twenty-six years ago when I first met Chris in the womb. My memories of that surreal encounter are a little blurred, but I often try to imagine what it must have been like in there; to be trapped, completely naked in a small dark room for nine months with someone you've never even been introduced to. I'm surprised I wasn't premature. What did we do in there, for Christ's sake? We probably had competitions on whose feet would grow the quickest, whilst curled up waiting to enter the world. It was seven o'clock in the morning when Chris finally decided to get the hell out of there. I couldn't quite get my act together and followed fifteen minutes later.

Due to a missed check-up, our parent's didn't know they were having twins. It's unimaginable what a shock that must have been, particularly for our poor mother who followed the trauma of childbirth number one with the news that another was on the way. I like to picture the midwife, dashing past my father in the waiting room with a bundle in her arms and shouting over her shoulder, "Congratulations Mr Raven - you have twins!" I would quite happily cut off my right leg with a blunt penknife, and feed it to a pack of hungry lions to see the expression on his face, as the realisation sunk in that he would have to buy a bigger pram and whole new set of baby clothes.

Being twins has always been a bonus, especially as kids. You get to live with a mate the same age, and most days if we weren't wiping dog shit on the side of our neighbour's house, or pulling our older brother's ears, we were fighting through the brambles in our back garden with toy guns and hunting each other down. Birthdays were fun, as we had a buddy to open our presents with – although, nowadays, it's more like a quick handshake, a punch on the arm and a pint down the pub. When we hit puberty we used to give each other money. I would say "happy birthday" to Chris and hand over a five-pound note and he would then return the favour. It was a perfect strategy to enable us to both give presents without being out of pocket, whilst at the same time supplying cash to blow on burgers, girls and cigarettes.

Being twins also has its disadvantages. Despite the fact that we look absolutely nothing like each other, our mother suffered unnecessary peer pressure when we were kids and felt obliged to dress us up in identical outfits at every formal occasion. Can you imagine how degrading that was? One minute we were the cool kids on the block, pulling girl's pigtails and cruising around the playground. The next we were forced to sit in front of a school camera, dressed in matching woolly tank tops and shirts with big cheesy collars (it was the 70s!) like a couple of circus monkeys. Hidden away in cupboards and framed on mantelpieces the length and breadth of England, there are dozens of pictures of Chris and I dressed identically, with our older brother sitting between us with a smug look on his face. To make matters worse we were also in great demand as pageboys at family weddings, skipping around holding hands in frilly velvet outfits and matching dicky bows. Not great for your street cred.

'...*Anyway,*' I laugh, removing the in-flight magazine from the seat in front. 'Seattle here we come!'

'Yes, indeedie. Lock-up-your-daughters!' Chris sings, grabbing a cup of water from a passing stewardess.

'Are you sure we've done enough research on all this?'

'What do you mean?'

'Well, there's nothing worse than being lost and jet-lagged in a big city. The airport's probably on the outskirts of town and slap-bang in the middle of a notorious gangland district.'

'Si, don't worry about it. We'll get a taxi or something.'

'I'm not worrying. I just want to make sure we know exactly what we're doing. I'm telling you now, I'll be seriously fucked off if we're robbed of our money and brutally murdered by a couple of crazed drug addicts in need of a quick fix.'

'Stop worrying - it'll be fine!'

'But aren't we supposed to have some kind of plan?'

'We do?'

'Do we?'

'Yeah.'

I frown. 'What plan?'

'The sit back, relax and see what happens when we get to Seattle, plan.'

Tutting, I pick up my orange juice off the foldaway tray, purse my lips and take a sip.

'Seriously.' Chris grins. 'The *plan* is to buy some wheels, right?'

'Fair enough, but have you thought about how the hell we're going to do that?'

'Chill out, would ya. We haven't even left British airspace and you're already freaking out. It's gonna be a piece of piss. We'll just find a garage and buy one of those big motor home things.'

'Don't be stupid! They're *well* expensive! We'll be lucky to get a VW camper van.'

'Really?'

'I nod, pursing my lips again. 'Yeah. In fact, we might only be able to afford a car.'

'*What?* There's no way I'm driving to LA cooped up in a rusty old motor.'

'Chris, we might have too!'

'You negative bastard. What if I get lucky one night and want to entertain a young lady?'

'You can put up the tent.'

'The tent? I'd rather Greyhound it and stay in motels.'

I sigh. 'And how are you going to afford that? You've got approximately, *NO FUCKING MONEY!*'

'Jesus Christ, Si! You're scaring the other passengers. And for your information I've got loads of money. I cleared my overdraft before I left.'

'Which means you have zero pounds, zero pence.'

He shakes his head. 'No. I have two thousand pounds, zero pence. So stop worrying and just go with the flow.'

Attempting to adjust my seat, I jerk backwards and

spill my entire drink over my crotch, a bit like Joan Collins in those old ads.

'*Bollocks!*' I spit, grabbing a pathetically thin paper napkin.

Chris snorts before flashing a smile at one of the cute stewardesses walking down the far aisle. I screw up the saturated napkin and toss it under my seat.

'Hey, Si! You might be a twat, but what you've just done takes a lot of guts.'

'What have I just done?'

'You know. Jacking it all in and stuff.'

'Does it?'

'Yeah. How many people say their dream is to pack up and get the hell out, but never get round to it?'

I glance down at the wet patch on my trousers. 'Shit loads I would imagine.'

'Love and work are dangerous games to play,' he grins. 'You've done the right thing.'

'Do you think so?'

'No, mate. I fucking know so.'

Legless in Seattle

Arriving late evening at Sea-Tac Airport, I follow Si to the immigration queue where a hard-faced official who looks like a man in drag, sends us off to a second stage of immigration.

Fearing the worst, I try to ignore the thought of a huge slavering immigration officer peering down at me, stretching a rubber glove over his hand and preparing to insert a fat finger up my arse. Fortunately, our trousers stay up and despite an intense search of our bags and a few probing questions, we escape without any unnecessary trauma.

'I can't believe you two are *twins*!' an officer remarks as she hands back our passports.

Si smiles nervously. 'Yeah. It's mad, isn't it?

'Well, you guys enjoy your visit now.'

'Thanks,' I reply, and with a sigh of relief we clumsily fall through the arrivals gate and make our North American entrance.

Studying a list of hotels at the information counter, we decide to spend our first night in a Super 8 Motel close to the airport on Pacific Highway 99. Bouncing around in the back of a mini bus for a while we arrive swiftly at the hotel, check in and head for room 206. Swiping the electronic key through the lock, I step inside and leap excitedly onto one of the gigantic king size beds. Si drops his bags on the floor and pops his head into the bathroom. He emerges with a huge smile on his face and skipping over to a large fitted wardrobe, he throws open the doors for inspection.

'Cool!' he cries, holding up a coat hanger. 'This room ain't bad.'

'What you talking about - it's *great*! There's a big telly and everything.'

Si rolls his eyes and picks up the remote off the dressing table. Sitting on the edge of the bed, he fires his best shot at the screen and the TV bangs into life. The reception is poor so he flicks between the hundreds of channels on offer. Apart from HBO, where we can just about see a blurred Sylvester Stallone taking on the world in *'Rambo: First Blood'*, the other 99 suffer from serious interference.

'Shall we raid the drinks cabinet and get hammered, then?'

'Does a monk spunk?' Si laughs, throwing the remote over his shoulder.

I shrug. 'Dunno. Does he?'

Poised and ready we scour the room, our mouths watering at the idea of a cold, refreshing beer.

'Where's the fridge?' I whisper.

'There isn't one.'

'There must be! How can they call this a Super 8 Motel if they don't supply a fridge full of booze - I mean, that's not very *super*, is it?'

Disgusted by the lack of provisions, we venture out in search of an all American bar. Spying a suitable looking establishment on the other side of a busy highway, we sprint for the entrance and sheepishly make our way inside.

'Hello?' Si calls, as we scan a deserted dinning room. 'It must be closed.'

At that moment, a young lad wearing a white shirt appears through swing doors at the far side of the room.

'Hi, there!' I cheerily wave. 'You open?'

Leaning his mop against a chair, he begins to walk over to us, but changes his mind and disappears back through the swing doors.

'Where's he gone?'

Si shrugs. 'I don't know. I suppose he's gone to find out if they're still open.'

He suddenly reappears, looking slightly out of breath.

'Yeah. We're open,' he drawls. 'What you after?'

'A drink would be good,' I shout back.

'Hold on.'

'Oh, for fuck's sake! Where's he gone now?'

'He must be checking to see if they serve drinks.'

'You're joking? What's the matter with this kid? Is he retarded?'

Once again he returns, this time leaning against the wall for support as he catches his breath.

'Yeah,' he coughs. 'We serve drinks - but we're closed right now.'

'You just said you were open!' I cry, desperation starting to get the better of me.

The kid coughs again before rubbing his temple. 'Did I?'

'My God! *Please*!' I cry. 'All we want is a beer.'

The kid frowns. 'A *beer*? Why didn't you say? Up those stairs for beer.'

We follow his gaze over to a narrow staircase, tucked into an alcove at the back of the restaurant.

I turn to Si and grin. 'Great! Let's check it out.'

Making our way up the stairs we slide our hands along the cold wall in the absence of any light.

'I can hear music. I think we're nearly there.'

'I frigging hope so,' Si grumbles. 'All I want is a drink, not an epic climbing adventure.'

Opening a door at the top of the staircase, we're blinded by bright lights as we enter a small, but lively drinking hole. Making a beeline for the bar, everyone stops talking, laughing, eating and drinking so they can all stare at us like we're prize bulls at a cattle auction. Feeling uncomfortable, we sit on bar stools and with huge false smiles, try to ignore the gawking faces. A tarty looking bleached blonde barmaid dressed in black leather trousers and a pink checked shirt, spots us and skips over.

'Hi, guys. What can I get ya?' she pouts squeezing her healthy looking breasts in our direction.

'Uh ... two beers, please.'

I watch with complete admiration as, in almost one graceful movement, she pirouettes over to the glasses, pulls down on the taps and skips back with two delicious looking beers.

'There you go handsome, that's eight bucks and a refill whenever you're ready.'

Paying for the drinks, I tear my eyes away from her butt cheeks, and follow Si to a dimly lit table in the farthest corner of the room.

'...Hold on a minute, Si. You're telling me, that if I'd continued with fashion photography and got my own studio, I would have turned into a pretentious prick?'

He nods. 'Yeah.'

'Really?'

'Uh-huh. All fashion photographers are pretentious, aren't they? It's part of the job description.'

'That doesn't mean I would have become one.'

'Yeah it does. You wouldn't have a choice.'

'How do you know?'

'I don't,' Si slurs, swaying in his chair.

'Well ... shut up, then.'

'Seriously Chris, it would have been a nightmare. Imagine assisting one of those shallow, arrogant photographers. To get ahead in that game you have to either know someone who is someone, which you don't, or kiss some serious ass, which I can't imagine you ever doing.'

'I did.'

'You kissed ass?'

'No, you fool. When I was a student, this fashion photographer came to my college looking for a slave to assist him on a few shoots.'

'And...?'

'He chose me.'

'Great!'

'No, not great. It was a complete nightmare! The guy was a right twat. Literally as soon as he picked up his camera he would turn into this angry...'

'Arrogant?'

'Arrogant ... tit. He'd make me look like a complete fool in front of the entire room - models, agents, publicists. Although I was hopeless, by the end I'd tripped over so many wires, exposed so much film and broke so much studio equipment that he banned me from ever coming within five miles of his career.'

Thinking back, it's actually quite surreal that I decided to spend three years of my life studying fashion photography. OK, so taking pictures of beautiful models might have had something to do with it. And, if I'm completely honest, it was also the only photography course I could get onto in London - despite it being incredibly well known throughout the fashion world.

Before escaping from our hometown in the Midlands, the sum total of my photographic experience, consisted of working for a photographer on our local town newspaper after leaving school. Terry Evans was a nice enough bloke, a little strange maybe, but I didn't take any notice of that, and soon realised his weirdness was probably the result of spending hours in the darkroom with large quantities of toxic developing chemicals and faulty ventilation. I wouldn't say it was the most exhilarating job in the world (working on a chicken farm probably ranks as the most fun I've had to date), but I did learn a hell of a lot from Terry - vital photographic skills. Such as how to pull girls by waving a big lens around, and how to change a roll of film in under five seconds. Terry was completely crazed (he's the only man alive who doesn't blink - ever), and there were moments when I'd catch myself feeling rather uncomfortable in his presence, especially in his darkroom. In his laboratory as he called it, he ranged from a 'mad scientist' concocting weird new chemicals in the name of dark arts, to 'war photographer', sprinting out of the office onto the battlefield, with lenses for weapons and Ilford black and white film for ammo. Well, it wasn't quite a battlefield, as such. We mostly took pictures of local news, like a milkman who'd won a whistling competition, a pancake race down the high street with a bunch of white-collared office workers, or of some old dear in a wheel chair who'd just turned three hundred. You know, that kind of thing.

Fashion photography promised to be a whole new ball game. The idea of taking pictures of beautiful women, rather than scraggy old councillors, sounded so much more glamorous. Well, at least that's what I thought. According to the college prospectus the institute was full to the brim with talented young students. Unfortunately, it failed to point out that they were also complete and utter tossers. Take, for example, the 'Serious Fashion Victims'. Fine, it was 'Fashion College' - I'll grant them that, but years before Reality TV, these victims were *convinced* a round-the-clock camera crew was following them. Or they thought they were in a movie or on a constant, never-ending catwalk.

One joker called Mark Richardson (for that was his name), honestly believed he looked cool dressed as a Mafia gangster. Wearing an Italian suit, a packet of red Marlboro cigarettes in his top pocket and his hair greased back, he confused his costume by including yellow shoes and a variety of dazzling multi-coloured shirts. Let's just say all that was missing was a red nose, a tricycle with a horn and a sub-machine gun that fired custard pies, and he could have easily won first prize in a 'best dressed clown competition'. On another occasion, as I strolled towards the library, I spied a student wearing a postman's coat, hat and carrying a Royal Mail satchel over his shoulder. I couldn't quite believe that he had taken fashion so literally, and more upsetting, he thought he looked cool. I know a lot of fashion trends passed me by, but I'm pretty sure Postman Pat was never considered a fashion icon.

As my course came to an end and graduation day approached, Patricia, my head tutor, asked me to step into her office. Patricia was in her late forties and lived in a complete and utter dream world. She redefined "being sucked in" and as head tutor for over a decade, she did everything to perpetuate her image as fashion guru and friend to the stars. Dressed that morning as Eva Peron, I remember sitting in her sweet smelling office, watching her self-consciously pull a folder out of a filing cabinet, slam the draw shut and perch herself on the edge of her desk. There was silence whilst she fixed me with her 'yes-I-know-you-want-to-fuck-me-but-that-really-wouldn't-be-very-professional' gaze.

'So, what are your plans?'

'Plans?' I frowned.

'Yes. Your pl-a-ns,' she drawled, pointlessly exaggerating the last word. 'I want to know what you're do-ing.'

'Well, I think once we've finished arranging our displays we're going for a few pints down the Lamb and Flag. You're very welcome to join us.'

Her eyes tilted back into her severe blond bun. 'Noooo, Chris. Your plans for the fu-ture?'

'As in work?'

'Yes! *Work*!' she snapped.

'Uh ... I'm still waiting for a response.'

'Don't lie. I know you haven't phoned my magazine contacts. Don't you want to be the next David Bailey?'

'David Bailey?'

She sighed. 'He's a photographer.'

I let that one go.

'To be honest with you, Patricia. It doesn't really appeal to me.'

'Excuse me?'

'Fashion photography. It doesn't *really* appeal to me as a career. Don't get me wrong, it's a great industry and all, but I've decided it's something I don't want to do anymore.'

Catching her breath and lowering her gaze, she gathered up her skirts and stood behind her swivel chair, either protecting herself from a clearly deranged student or protecting me from a possible violent assault.

'Why have you spent three years on this course, if you're not going to pursue fashion photography as a career?'

'It's nothing personal against you or the Institute, Patricia. It's just I've decided to travel for a while.'

'*Travel*?'

'Yes.'

'Why?'

'Well, I was chatting to a girl in the canteen a few weeks ago. She was telling me about the Rocky Mountains and the beaches of California, and it got me thinking that there's an entire world out there just waiting for me to explore.'

'But you've been a good student, Chris. You'd be throwing all that away. You will miss your *ONLY CHANCE*,' she gasped, trying to breathe through her anger to prevent hyperventilating.

Even though I had completely let Patricia down, I left her office that day feeling utterly relieved to have finally told someone about my new plans. I simply wasn't ready to commit myself to a career, certainly not in the competitive world of fashion photography, and looking for temp work the very next day I felt confident I had made the right decision.

$1,500 for a Tank

Opening one eye, I peer out into the dimly lit motel room. Chris snores loudly beneath his sheets, and with blurred vision and air-con blasting it's impossible to tell the time of day. Summoning the strength to climb out of bed, I crawl weakly over to the window, straighten my back and draw the curtains along speedy runners. Glaring white light blinds me, and I shield my eyes to get my first good look at America. Dodge trucks, RV trailers and an A-Team van clutter the carpark outside, all drenched in summer sunshine, and feeling inspired I wonder what our vehicle might look like - how it must sit somewhere at this very moment waiting for us to pass by.

A white car pulls up outside the window and without my contact lenses, I squint hard to make out the blurred letters printed across the door.

'Police,' I whisper.

Fixing my stare on the confused brow of the uniformed officer at the wheel, my eyes spring open as he nudges his partner and points in my direction. Standing exposed, pale and thin in the frame of the window, my tattered boxer shorts hang loosely from my bony hips like a loincloth and, at a quick glance, I resemble a petrified Jesus cowering beneath the heavens in a biblical painting.

Watching the expressions on their faces change from surprise to mirth, I dive to the floor in a bid for salvation and with my eyes tightly shut, I prey for this humiliation to be over.

Throwing himself at the curtains, Chris sprints past and I feel a slap to the back of my head, 'top spin' style, as he falls dramatically back onto the bed.

'What the hell are you doing? That was a cop car, you prick!'

'You bastard,' I laugh, cringing with embarrassment. 'I'm as blind as a bat without my lenses.'

'They should've arrested you for being too white.'

'Piss off,' I smirk, clambering to my feet. 'In a few days I'll be golden brown.'

'In a few days you'll be red as fuck!'

Rubbing his freshly shaven head, Chris looks tougher than usual. He used to be a skinny bastard like me, but he's filled out considerably over the past couple of years. With olive skin and dark brown eyes compared to my blue, we don't look anything like brothers - let alone twins and I prefer it that way.

Scratching my chin I sit up. 'Hey, Chris! I've been thinking.'

'Congratulations!'

'No, seriously. Seeing as we're a couple of dumb-asses, maybe we should pay a mechanic to help us look for a decent van?'

'Really? Sounds expensive.'

I shake my head. 'Nah. All we have to do is wave a few dollars under some dude's nose, and *bingo* - we've got ourselves a perfect set of wheels. At least we'll get something that works.'

'Yeah ... I mean, no ... I mean, *whatever!* Let's do it,' he grins, grabbing his towel off the back of a chair.

'Really?'

Chris is not known for his relaxed attitude to money.

'Yeah. Let's get some breakfast!'

Men with a mission, we march along a raging highway towards a car lot on the distant horizon. Multicoloured bunting hangs motionless until disturbed by the whoosh of a passing car. Spying a round face peeking out from the window of a portacabin, we pretend not to notice as we pass a row of vehicles and pause out of politeness at each one.

Chris frowns. 'These are *well* expensive!'

'Yeah. I can't see any camper vans, either. Shall we carry on?'

Speaking too soon, a large gentleman fills the door to the cabin and waves merrily in our direction.

'Hi there!' he shouts crossing the forecourt at surprising speed considering his heavy load. 'I'm John - welcome to Larry's Cars.'

Grinning falsely, he shakes our hands with sticky palms.

'Where you guys from?'

'England,' Chris smiles.

'I thought I heard an accent,' even though we hadn't said a word.

'Whereabouts?'

'Uh ... London.'

'London? Oh ...yer. I went to London a few years back. Hey, do you know Lie-chester Square?'

'You mean Leicester Square?'

'Come again.'

'Its pronounced Leicester Square.'

John furrows his brow. 'That's what I said. Anyway, I saw some theatre show there with my wife. Can't remember the damn name of it. Lots of men dancing around like girls. Absolute bullshit, but she had a good time.'

Weighing around eighteen stone, John's piggy little eyes hide behind round, gold frame glasses. Dressed casually in a lime green polo shirt, white sports socks and sneakers, he stands with his hands in the pockets of his lightly stained khaki trouser shorts. Immediately irritated by his presence, I know we're not going to get along.

He strokes his ratty looking goatee beard, and informs us that most of his cars are brand new so probably well out of our price range.

'We've got a big green monster out the back,' he nods, pointing over his huge shoulder. 'Which I think will be more in your price range.'

On that note, he storms off without waiting to find out what our price range actually is. With little to loose, we follow him round the back of the office to an overgrown yard. Hoping to discover an abandoned, but lovingly preserved VW camper van, our illusions are swiftly shattered by the sight of a rusty estate car with its wheels sunk into the ground. John leans on the car to get his breath back and I notice the side panel buckle slightly under his weight.

'I know it doesn't look like much,' he wheezes, fumbling inside his pockets for the keys, 'but she's a great runner.'

He pulls out a bunch of keys and begins forcing one of them into the rusty lock. Using all of his considerable weight he prises open the door, which hangs heavily on its hinges. We stand back in utter disbelief, as he climbs headfirst inside and begins tearing at grass growing through the dashboard.

'Is he serious?' Chris whispers.

Distracted, I stare at his thrusting ass which, jerking from side-to-side, appears to talk to us from the driver's door.

'You won't find anything better than this beauty for less than two thousand dollars,' it informs us. 'I'd rather sell you one of these than a modern vehicle any darn day.' He turns towards us and grins. 'I mean, you guys can see it's a classic, right?'

We both nod and quickly flash him a smile.

By contorting his huge body, he manages to squeeze into the driver's seat with his stomach pressing hard against the steering wheel, and looks over at us with a bright red face.

'So, shall I get the jump leads, guys?'

I step forward. 'It's not quite what we had in mind.'

'Sure thing, fellas,' he says, looking disappointed, but not deterred. 'Darn shame, though. This vehicle is gonna – '

'Sorry, mate.' Chris cuts in abruptly. 'We're off.'

I turn to reprimand him, but realise I totally agree.

'*NO! WAIT!*' John cries, struggling to free his gut from behind the wheel. 'I can help you guys.'

Turning on our heels, I try not to laugh, as we start to walk purposefully across the yard to the sound of John's desperate cries for help. Catching Chris's eye, I snort with laughter and pick up the pace until we both spon-taneously break into a run.

'Do you think we should go back and give him a hand?' Chris shouts.

I shake my head. 'Nah … let's fucking leave him!'

With arms and legs flailing we run across the car lot, pushing each other to try and win the race. Like we are nine again.

* * *

Watching Si march aggressively ahead, I pause in the sweltering heat of the day and rest for a moment against

28

the bonnet of a beautiful old Lincoln. Even though it's only nine o'clock in the morning, the temperate is over eighty degrees and the vehicles on the highway look hazy in the distance. Opening my rucksack, I fish around inside for a bottle of water. Noticing that I'm lagging behind, Si walks back towards me.

'Come on!' he sighs. 'Let's keep moving!'

'What's the rush?'

'What do you mean, "what's the rush?" Think about it! The quicker we find a van. The quicker we can hit the road.'

'If I carry on at this pace I'll die of heat exhaustion.'

'You pussy!'

'Fuck off! It's hot, you little shit!'

'Slap a bit of suntan lotion on your face and drink some water. I'm sure you'll be fine.'

'Si, just sit down a minute and chill out, will ya. You're stressing me out.'

'Hey ... *look*!'

'What?'

'Look behind you. There it is! Oh, thank you Lord!'

Twisting round, I see the entrance to a tatty garage surrounded by mountains of old tyres and abandoned cars. And a van.

'Chris, our prayers have been answered. Heaven has shown us the way!'

'I wouldn't go that far.'

'But look at the way it shines!'

'Fuck the shine - look at the colour!'

'What about it?'

'It's cack brown.'

'So?'

'It's not very *cool*, is it?'

'Who cares? The condition is the most important thing.'

'Yeah, but we're not going to pull many girls driving

that, are we?'

'We can pull girls on foot. Come on! Let's at least take a look.'

Peering through the van's tinted windows, I suddenly notice a greasy looking mechanic walking towards us in the reflection of the glass.

'You fellas need any help?' he mutters unenthusiastically.

'Hi. Is this van for sale?' I ask.

'Uh-huh,' he grunts.

'Great. How much is it?'

'One thousand eight-hundred.'

All three of us stand in silence. I look at Si, Si looks at me and the mechanic stares at his worn old boots.

'So ... does it work?'

'Uh-huh.'

Unsure what to do next, I glance around the yard and scratch my head.

'Hmm...' I ponder, tapping the bodywork.

Looking over at Si for support, he walks around the van and gently kicks the back tyre.

Clearly owning two cars through school had made no impact on our knowledge of the internal combustion engine. We didn't realise you needed an internal combustion engine until we'd blown the first one up. Back then, as long as it had four wheels, a stereo and plenty of room in the back, we didn't care if the engine was held together with string.

'*THE BONNET!*' Si suddenly yells. 'Can we please look under the bonnet?'

The mechanic throws a cold, blank look in my direction whilst removing dirt from under his fingernails with a rusty screwdriver.

'Don't they call it the hood?' I offer.

I see a pale glimmer of recognition in his eyes before he lowers the brim of his Yankees baseball cap, and in slow motion he reaches an arm through the driver's open window and pops the hood.

We both peer unconvincingly at the engine, and after a few painful seconds, we agree that it looks ... uh ... good.

'Can we take it for a test drive?' I risk asking.

'Uh-huh.'

Slamming the bonnet shut it occurs to me how trusting he is to let two foreigners speed off with one of his vehicles. But at the end of the day he probably doesn't give a shit.

Like lightening, Si climbs into the passenger seat.

'What you doing?'

'Well, I'm not driving!'

Unhappy about taking on any form of responsibility (at all, ever), I snatch the keys out of his hand.

'OK, but you owe me big time, you long haired hippy.'

I've never driven an automatic before, and starting the engine I release the handbrake and we shoot across the forecourt, kangarooing out onto the highway. To the sound of blasting horns and Simon's screams, I realise it would be better all round if I move over to the other side of the road. Swerving, I pull dangerously into the right hand slow lane.

'*CHRIS, YOU PRICK! GET OFF AT THE NEXT EXIT!*'

'It's an automatic! I don't know how to drive an AUTO-MATIC!'

'*RED LIGHT!*' Si cries, covering his eyes and getting into the crash position.

Slamming on the brakes, we slide to a halt inches from the back of a bright orange school bus.

'Jesus Christ!' I laugh maniacally. 'At least we know the brakes work!'

Deciding that it's probably best if we quit while we're still ahead, I make it back to the car lot and stall stylishly outside the office.

'What do you think, Chris? Shall we get it? We need to decide. The mechanic dude's walking over.'

'Well...?'

'Let's buy it! We can learn how to drive it later.'

The mechanic leans both arms on my open window. He opens his mouth to say something, but changes his mind - or just can't be arsed.

I tap the steering wheel nervously. 'We'll take it!'

'Uh-huh,' he nods, forcing a smile.

Entering his office, which is really more of a shack tacked onto the side of his workshop, he gestures for us to take a seat in two flimsy foldaway chairs. Struggling to get comfortable, we watch as he tries to organise himself by rummaging through a huge pile of folders on his desk, and then squeezing past a partly dismantled motorbike, he begins flicking through screwed up piles of paper on the floor. A dirty face suddenly appears at the workshop door belonging to a young kid in green overalls.

'JAKE! GET THE FUCK OUT OF HERE!' the mechanic yells, and leaping to his feet he slams the door in the kid's face. 'Little bastard! He knows he's not allowed in here.'

Eventually finding the relevant documents, he collects them together and hands it all over to Si.

'Sign here,' he points, leaving an oily fingerprint on the page. 'How do you want to pay?'

We've got one thousand five hundred dollars in cash,' Si chips in.

He frowns. 'One thousand five hundred dollars in cash?'

'Yeah - in *cash*,' Si winks.

Thinking real hard and for several minutes he finally agrees to the cash. We hand over the green stuff before he changes his mind, and bidding him farewell jump into our new van.

'What a fucking result!' I cry, caressing the steering wheel.

'Too right! We've just saved ourselves three hundred dollars.'

Turning out onto the highway, I concentrate on the traffic. Throwing a quick glance in the rear view mirror, I see the garage disappearing into the distance and blinking in disbelief, I'm convinced I see our sour faced friend rubbing his hands together and doing a little dance.

Bear Bells

Interference blasts from the radio.

'What do you want to listen to, Chrissy boy - Country and Western or plain old Rock 'n' Roll?'

'Sorry, Dolly! You're a great singer - I *love* your hits and *adore* your tits, but give me some Rock 'n' fuckin' Roll, baby!'

Turning the dial, Bon Jovi fills the van with 'Living on a Prayer' and we feel compelled to join in.

Our new home feels massive inside, and deciding to explore I release the seat belt from my big chunky arm-chair, and dive into the vast space at the back like an excited kid at Christmas. Lying here on the brown furry carpet of our very own Ford Aerostar, I close my eyes for a second and savour the sensation of freedom. I find it hard to believe that we arrived in Seattle less than 24 hours ago and turning to the window, I see the Cascade Mountains on the horizon and the crowded forests of pine rising up into the hills. Road signs familiar from a million movies litter the highway - one pointing to Vancouver, another to Portland, and I breath a sigh of relief as it starts to sink in that we've left London far behind.

The day I resigned from my job at a big American internet company in London, has to be the most magnificent moment of my life. Truly magical. Finally, after four years of sitting slumped in front of a computer, I felt the corporate dandruff blow freely out of my long scruffy hair.

Despite climbing the dizzy heights from humble news desk assistant to big shot internet Producer, I'd begun to realise that it was either time to drift into management, or move on. My life just seemed to stop being exciting, and I felt desperate to escape the mundane world of the office. I longed to travel.

I found handing in my resignation to my boss hugely satisfying, closely followed by the thrill of telling my work colleagues, my friends and pretty much anybody who'd listen. For weeks afterwards people would ask me about my plans and whether I had a new job lined up. I'd tell them I was going travelling. It was a straightforward enough answer, but most people would stand there for a few seconds looking puzzled and then shoot a quick look of concern. They'd ask "where to?" and I'd reply "America" and they'd reply "where in America?" and I'd reply "the north west" and they'd reply "where in the north west?" and I'd reply "Washington state", and they'd reply "ah ... to see the White House". I had this conversation with just about everybody in the office.

I'm pretty sure my immediate boss was glad to see me go. Our personalities had clashed the moment we set eyes on each other, but my colleagues seemed genuinely sad to say goodbye. The obligatory leaving card was filled with messages ranging from the envious, "You lucky fuck! Darrell," (nice bloke), to the bitter, "Hope you enjoy yourself and this doesn't harm your career. Eddy," (divorced at 28) and everything in between. "Have a lovely future and a marvellous time, hugs and bugs Jonathan xx," (closet homosexual), "May your path be bright and beautiful, may the people you meet be kind and giving and may the stories you tell your Grandchildren be wise and wonderful. Christian Von Setten," (pretentious wanker).

My life has changed direction beyond all recognition and I'm not scared. Now I'm jobless, you'd think it would be natural for me to be worried about my future, mentally preparing my CV - thinking about what my next career move will be. But I'm not. I've left behind what career I had. End of story. Or should I say, beginning of story.

Spying a camping store in the small industrial town of Everett, we pull over and pick up a few things we might need in the remote wilderness. Entering the brightly-lit building, we stand back in awe at the dazzling world of outdoor survival equipment – an Aladdin's cave for game hunters, self-respecting trekkers or anyone in search of adventure.

'Chris,' I whisper, nudging his arm as he looks up in amazement at a large moose's head.

'Yeah?'

'Let's go shopping!'

Like Little Red Riding Hood in a field of flowers, we skip and dance down the aisles with our baskets, gathering gas canisters, plastic cutlery, cups, plasters and batteries for my personal stereo. Surviving in the wild is certainly a lot easier nowadays, with everything on offer from heat in a can to self-chilling lager and freeze-dried roast dinners small enough to fit down your pants.

Approaching the counter, a painfully skinny old woman greets us with a crooked smile.

'Wait a minute, Chris. Didn't you read something about getting a bell to warn off bears when you're out trekking?'

'Oh, yeah! I'll ask if they've got them.'

The woman's eyes are sunk deep into her fragile skull. Wearing outrageously bright red lipstick and thick foundation, she isn't fooling anyone that she's still a young princess.

'Excuse me. Do you have any bear bells for sale?'

Holding her stomach while coughing hard into her other hand, she looks incredulously at Chris.

'Say again, son?'

'Bear bells.'

'I don't know what them are, son.'

'Oh. I think they must be bells for scaring off bears.'

She starts to shakily place our goods into brown paper bags. 'Sorry son, you've lost me,' she grimaces, exposing her nicotine-stained teeth.

'That's weird. I read something about them on the internet and it advised buying a bell in case, well … you know. In case a bear attacks you.'

'The internet?' she spits, wiping saliva from her chin. 'Listen, son. I've worked in this store for over thirty years and I've never had anyone ask me for bells, or internets to scare off bears. I'll get my Al from out back.'

'*NO*! You don't have to do that!' I cry. 'It's really not important. We'll manage without one.'

She tilts her head to one side and stares into my eyes. 'You sure? He's just out back.'

'Absolutely *no* need,' Chris adds firmly.

'To be honest,' she wheezes. 'A bell ain't gonna do much if a thousand pound grizzly is charging at ya. You fellas thought about buying a gun?'

I turn to Chris and glance over at the rifles on the wall, not sure if the old dear is winding us up.

'Thanks all the same, but we'll risk it,' Chris replies, and grabbing our stuff from the counter, we head swiftly towards the exit.

Armed with everything necessary to survive the American wilderness, Chris unpacks our new equipment whilst I reverse the van out onto the main road and head for the supermarket next door.

Grabbing a trolley we race through the automatic doors and, in a highly organised fashion, begin to work our way round. Zipping past frozen veg, we hit canned foods, stock up on baked beans and tinned spaghetti in tomato sauce before doing a handbrake turn to narrowly avoid a head on crash with a rather religious looking woman, who is strangely attractive.

'Oh ... I'm sorry.'

'That's OK,' she smiles flirtatiously, whilst fingering the silver cross hanging around her neck.

We both watch with admiration, as her pert backside wiggles off down the aisle.

'Dirty bitch!' Chris grins. 'It's women like that who make me glad to be alive.'

'Damn, right. Come on! Let's stay focused on food. Shall we get some canned meatballs and ravioli?'

'Yeah, and how about some macaroni cheese and frankfurter sausages?'

Filling up the trolley with a dozen tins of mixed vegetables, we swing around the next bend and hit cereal, tea and coffee. Chris grabs a 10 pack of variety cereals, and as we ponder over whether to get 80 Saver tea bags or 160, we're surprised by a purposeful nudge to our trolley from the sexy minx we passed a moment ago.

'Excuse me, guys. Would one of you mind reaching up for a pack of green tea? These shelves are *far* too high.'

'Absolutely no problem,' Chris stutters, leaping to her request.

'Are you from England?' she asks, fucking me with her eyes behind a sharply cut fringe.

'Yes. Near London,' I playfully reply, and noticing that her collar-less blouse is buttoned tightly to her throat, I wonder if she enjoys the discomfort.

'A while back we had a young student from Canterbury

staying with a family in our Parish; such a handsome young man...'

Nodding my head, I imagine her dressed head to toe in black leather clutching a bible in one hand and cracking a whip in the other. I'll bet that young fella from Canterbury got more from her Parish than he bargained for.'

'Have you ever been there?'

'I'm sorry - what was that?'

'To Canterbury. Have you been there?'

'Uh ... yes,' I lie, having never been near the place. 'It's a very beautiful city.'

'Well, if you're ever in the neighbourhood of the Church of the Evangelicals, please make sure you swing by and say hi. You're always welcome in Jesus' house,' she winks.

Thanking her, we part company. Noticing Chris chewing away at his bottom lip, I know similar filth has been running through his mind - only far, far worse.

Welcome to Freeway

Si butters bagels on the back seat and mumbles something about cheap margarine, as cars line up bumper-to-
bumper along the congested highway.

I notice a sleek, beautiful convertible cruise up beside
us. Behind the wheel is a businessman sporting a pair
of enormous clip-on shades, and if it wasn't for the sexy
new mobile phone against his ear, he could easily pass
for having just stepped out of the Eighties - cheesy
Michael Douglas *Wall Street* stockbroker style.

'Poor bloke,' I mutter, as he blasts his horn at the car in
front.

'You what?' Si replies, slapping a slice of ham into a
bagel.

'I was just thinking how shit it must be to battle
through this traffic everyday.'

'Fuck that for a game of soldiers. Fighting to get on the
tube was bad enough.'

'Don't remind me.'

'But you always seemed so relaxed in London.'

'At college, maybe. But not while working for that
company in the City when I was saving up to go travelling.'

'What, Bits and PCs?'

'Nah, that was years ago. It was VSM Ltd. Video Screens and Machines. '

In London, I'd often catch myself knocking people to one side on the tube, or tutting behind some poor tourist frantically trying to work out how to buy a ticket from a London Transport ticket machine. I was a ticking bomb just waiting to explode.

Two days after graduating from Fashion College, I found myself working for this telesales company in Cannon Street. It was a million miles from the fake glamour of fashion photography, but throwing myself into a temp job was the only way to make my escape from London and get myself travelling in the shortest possible time.

The majority of my days at VSM were spent learning effective sales techniques from an overweight slob called Darren. Most of the intensive training consisted of Darren walking past my desk on the way to the chocolate machine, reminding me to "sell the sizzle not the sausage". He did this about 35 times a day. My boss wasn't any better and as his desk was literally on top of mine, he would listen to and comment on every single call I made. He was an ex-Reuters man, a typical city bloke who'd remained single until the last possible moment, and then acquired a wife and moved to Weybridge. A deeply unfunny man, he insisted on shouting "Suit you, sir" at any given opportunity, always expecting me to reply with a hearty "No, suit you." I never did.

One Monday morning, after about three weeks of work, I phoned Si from a phone box near the office.

'I have to leave! This telesales job is killing me.'

'Hey, come on! How bad can it be?'

'Si, this is serious! My eyes hurt, my throat's sore and

41

my work colleagues are complete knob heads. What the *hell* am I doing? I mean, I'm wearing a shirt and tie, for Christ's sake.'

'Hang in there, bud. Just go back to the office and bite the bullet. Think of the cash.'

I slowly lowered the receiver. Taking on board what Si had said I thought about it really hard. Should I go back to the office? *Should* I? Think about the cash. I munched on a Lion Bar and thought about it ... nah. I walked back towards Cannon Street tube station and never darkened VSM's doorway again.

OK. So money was very important to me, but it was the only thing I needed, not bullshit, or God forbid - a career. The following Monday, I found myself working as a shift worker for a pharmaceutical re-packing centre in Camden - much more my style. Well, not quite. Not only did I have to go through the humiliation of wearing a blue hair net on my head all day (just like me old Nan at bedtime), which at first was horrendous. I also had to experience brain dead jobs like putting Prozac, Temazepam and diarrhoea tablets into bottles and screwing on the lids. Although the job did weaken my sanity, it was flexible hours and attracted a truly bizarre cast of characters. Pearl was an enormous woman from St. Lucia who hated her job, the manager and basically anything with a penis, but despite this, she smiled continuously from 9am to 6pm. Then there was Des, a fifty-six year old dude with a heart of gold and some obvious mental challenges, possibly brought on by working in the same place for forty years. He spent much of his time flapping his arms and clucking like a chicken, but that's the Pharmaceutical industry for you. Free drugs ain't everyone's idea of heaven, but it got these people through the working day. The days were long, but there was a radio in our windowless room that helped to pass the time. Unfortunately, Des liked to listen to a dodgy local station, so I was tortured for the whole eight hours by Pearl's moans, Des' weird squawking noises and one awful love song after another.

Glancing back at the businessman in the sports car he looks exhausted, a bright red face suggesting that his heart is dealing with far more than it can handle. He pounds his horn and I wonder what's going on in his confused mind. He's probably running late for an important meeting at a large finance house in the city - a meeting that could make or break his career. Or he's returning to another boring afternoon in the office, under the harsh glare of strip lighting and humming of computers, where his boss, who's ten years his junior, has asked him to work late if he's to stand any chance of a promotion. There's not even enough time to take lunch anymore, so he joins the rest of the suckers and eats at his desk.

There are some people in this world that seem to get a real buzz from stress. I can only assume that it makes them feel important in some way. All I know is, the last thing I want to experience is a heart attack, and whilst lying in a hospital bed attached to a beeping machine, realise that it was all an utter waste of time and meant jack shit.

As the traffic clears in the fast lane, the black convertible zooms off into the distance. Passing the small town of Freeway, I feel a tap on my shoulder and Si passes me a fat ham bagel. Admiring its size, I sink my teeth in, but stop mid-bite when I hear a loud knocking sound coming from the front wheel. Flicking on the hazard lights, I swerve the van over to the hard shoulder. Jumping out, I expect the worst, but much to my relief the tyres all seem to be intact.

'*I DON'T UNDERSTAND!*' I shout to Si over the roar of the traffic. '*I'M SURE IT SOUNDED LIKE A PUNTURE!*'

Praying that the problem is minor, I jump back into the safety of the van and continue to the town of Freeway, where we pull over in a lay-by next to the burnt out shell of a car. Running round to the side of the van, Si grabs the tools wedged under our bags and attempts to loosen the wheel nuts.

'Bollocks!' he cries, throwing the spanner to the ground. 'It's too small for the bolts! That bastard has sold us a van with the wrong sized spanner!'

'Leave it, then! The tyres not punctured. It seems fine.'

'Chris, we can't drive into the remote mountains with a dodgy wheel. It'd be suicide! I think we should stay here tonight and get it checked out in the morning.'

I dart glances around the lay-by. 'Here!'

Si nods. 'Yeah. In this town.'

'You can forget that for a start.'

'Why the fuck not?'

'There's no way I'm staying in this shit hole. Look around you, Si. We'll be hijacked and killed within seconds.'

'Don't be stupid. Come on, at least we're not in the middle of nowhere.'

'There's nothing wrong with the tyre! Something must have got stuck inside the wheel arch. We've just driven it over a hundred miles - it's fine!'

'It's *not* fine! We haven't got the right fucking spanner - it's too dangerous!'

'Chill out, will ya?'

'No! Fuck you! Jesus, you and your "life's-too-short-what's-the-worst-that-can-happen?" attitude. I'll tell you what can happen, shall I? We could fucking die in those mountains and never be found again.'

I stare at the driver's window and draw a line through the dirt with my finger. 'Have you finished?'

Si shrugs. 'I might have. Look - you need to grow up, Chris. I'm not going to risk my life because you couldn't be arsed to wait until tomorrow.'

'I promise you. This van is in good condition. It's as tough as old boots, mate. Let's just keep driving.'

'If we break down you're going to regret saying that.'

'So maybe it's a bad idea, but do you know what I think?'

'What?' he sighs.

'I think we should risk it!'

* * *

Driving along a thick avenue of trees, Chris bops his head in time to the music. Signs appear in our headlights warning of deer crossing, and it feels like we're making progress as we journey through the night, deep into the backcountry. The great, white Mount Rainer appears illuminous in the distance as we are pulled in its direction. The air is heavy with the smell of pine, which gives me courage to kick off my trainers for a while and rest my smelly feet on the dashboard.

Approaching a steep hill, I squint as our headlights struggle to penetrate the darkness and picking the road map off the floor, I begin to study it for the first time in what seems like ages.

'Chris, are you sure this is the right way?'

'We're just following the signs to the Mount Rainer National Park, aren't we?'

'Are we?'

'Yeah.'

'Didn't they disappear after we left the highway?'

'I don't know. You're the one with the shagging map.'

I place the map in the side pocket. 'I haven't looked at it for ages.'

'Why not?'

'Because I thought you were following the road signs!'

I get the map out again. 'If I'm not mistaken, this road will take us up and behind the mountain. We should come across a town called Ecclestone soon.'

'I hope you're right, because this is a mother of a...'

'*WATCH THE EDGE*!' I scream, as the road drops sharply away from my passenger window.

'*YOU TWAT*!' Chris yells.

'*What*?'

'You scared the shit out of me!'

'Well, be more careful! The wheels nearly went over the edge.'

'I was miles away, you fool!'

The smell of our burning brakes fills the night air as we descend the hill at an impossible angle, reaching the bottom after a good thirty minutes of near death corners. Spying a gas station at the junction of an empty road, Chris slowly pulls in and turns off the engine.

'I refuse to get stressed here, but where are we?' he cries, slamming his fist on the steering wheel.

'I don't know. If it wasn't for you, we could be sitting in a cosy bar in Freeway now necking beers and talking shit.'

'What, like you are now?'

I nod. 'Yeah. Like me right fucking now!'

'Oh ... fuck off, Si.'

'*NO*! *FUCK YOU*!' I scream psychotically.

Chris's face contorts with anger. 'You're *such* a cunt! I knew you'd be a nightmare to travel with. Why the fuck didn't you stay in London, you pretentious prick!'

'I should've! At least I wouldn't have you in my face all the time.'

'What is it with you? It's like you think the whole world's against you. Well, get real tosser - no one gives a shit!'

Silence consumes the van.

'I don't need this crap,' I mutter, opening the door.

'That's handy, *BECAUSE NEITHER DO I!*'

Slamming the door hard behind me, rage pumps through my veins as I race across the dimly lit forecourt towards the run down shop. Inside there's little more than a musty smell and a few rows of half-filled shelves. Faded posters cover the greasy walls and a life-size cut out of Superman, standing proud with his arms folded and his hair perfectly styled, leans against an empty video display. A sole videocassette lies facedown and alone on the top shelf and curious to know what's hot in these parts I pick it up. To my surprise it's not *Terminator* or *Nine and _ Weeks*, but those crazy girls Goldie Hawn, Bette Midler and Diane Keaton in *The First Wives Club*. 'Don't get mad, get everything!' blazes from the cover. An odd choice for this hard little shop in the middle of nowhere, but even hicks must need a bit of cheesy chick-flick comedy every now and then.

A great slob of a man crouches behind the till.

'Good evening,' I mumble.

He looks up, rather flustered considering I'm the only customer for miles.

'Can I get twenty Marlboro Lights, please?'

Grabbing the last packet off the shelf he throws them onto the counter.

I reach over and take a blueberry muffin off a randomly stacked pile on the counter.

'I don't suppose you know where Ecclestone is, do you?'

'Where's you tryin' to get?' my vile new friend replies in a thick local accent, as he wipes the back of his hand on his vest and sniffs.

'Oh … Mount Rainer.'

As he points out of the window, I catch the faint, nauseating smell of bleach drift over from his direction. I ignore it until I notice dried up tissue paper stuck along his index finger. The smell of bleach, dried up tissue paper – what's this bloke doing? Suddenly, I catch a glimpse of a magazine on the floor by his chair, open at a page with a buxom brunette fingering her anus. I try to hide my disgust and quickly put the muffin back on the pile.

'Well, if you goes that way,' he stammers, 'you can get on highway twenty and follow the signs.'

'And if I go that way?'

'That takes ya to the quarry and Sandy's yard. You don't wonna be goin' that way.' He shakes his head. 'No sir. Not that way.'

'Ah, OK, perfect. Thanks a lot.'

Utterly appalled to be alone with a man, who's just ejaculated over himself, I leave my change on the counter and swiftly return to the safety of the van.

Agreeing to put our differences behind us, Chris strikes up the van and we head off towards the highway. Thundering through the night and eating up mile after mile, we find great comfort in the fact that events cannot get any worse.

We stop at traffic lights and wait patiently for the lights to change.

'Déjà vu,' I mutter. 'All these shitty little towns look the same.'

Looking suddenly worried, Chris turns to me. 'Yeah, they do a bit.'

'What's wrong?'

'Nothing. Look, Si,' he grins, trying hard to look apologetic. 'I'm sorry for being a prick earlier. Maybe I'm a bit tired.'

'Don't worry about it. That's the good thing about us two, whenever we disagree it's all forgotten about five minutes later. That's how we're able to travel together in these conditions. I mean, we managed in the womb without killing each other, didn't we?'

He nods. 'Yeah, but you didn't have iron bars to hit me

with or guns to shoot me with in the womb.'

'What'd mean?'

'Well, put it this way. If I said that we've just spent the last three hours driving in a complete circle, you'd remain calm, right?'

'Uh ... let me think about this. *NO!*'

Chris points across the road at another burnt out car in a lay-by, very similar to where we had parked earlier. I feel immediately sick. Rubbing my temple I take a deep breath.

'We've just spent the last three hours driving in a complete circle. We're back where we started!' Chris whispers, clenching his teeth.

'We can't be!' I murmur, holding my chest as I prepare to hyperventilate.

'This town doesn't just look like Freeway. It *is* Freeway!'

Freeway is a town I had hoped I would never see again. Spying the glowing logo of a Jack in the Box, Chris suggests we feed our pain and grab something to eat.

'Here you go,' he smiles.

'What's this?'

'My money.'

'I know it's your money, numb nuts. Why have you given it to me?'

'It should be just enough for one of those big whopper meal things. Oh, and make it a Coke not a Pepsi. I hate Pepsi.'

'Think again, pal. I'm not getting it.'

Grunting, Chris pops his seat belt and swings his legs out of the door, but before his feet even touch the tarmac, he sees a gang of dodgy looking kids in baseball caps leave the restaurant. In one swift movement, he's back in the van and locking the door as we watch the gang of kids punching and karate kicking each other for their own amusement.

'I knew this was going to happen,' Chris mutters. 'We're going to die in this God-forsaken hole.'

'Don't be stupid! They can't be a day over fourteen. They're just kids, for Christ sake.'

'Si, we're very vulnerable here. This is an empty car park at midnight and we've got shit loads of money on us.'

'It's all in travellers cheques and, anyway, what they gonna do? Give us Chinese burns and call us names? Ooh ... I'm *really* scared. I've got a good mind to go over there and give them all a clip round the ear.'

'Don't be a dick! You'd either get a bottle over the head or a bullet up the arse. Those kids could easily be carrying guns.'

'All *right*! I take your point.'

'Kids that age are fearless. They're likely to show off in front of their mates.'

'Chris – I said OK! Let's get out of here before they see us.'

Reaching for the key, Chris turns the ignition. The engine kicks into life, spitting out exhaust fumes and growling loud enough to wake the dead. Looking up, I notice the kids have stopped karate-kicking each other and are now starring right at us.

'*QUICK!*' I cry, sinking into my seat. '*GET ME THE FUCK OUT OF HERE!*'

Brandishing glass bottles above their heads, the kids begin to run towards us, and I realise pretty quickly that they're not interested in a friendly conversation.

Chris whacks the van into reverse.

'*MOVE! MOVE! MOVE!*'

A bottle hits the roof of the van with a loud thud, quickly followed by another flying missile, which ricochets off the back window before smashing onto the tarmac. Spinning the van out onto the main road we burn off in a shower of glass.

Ray Mears is a God

A strong smell of pipe tobacco hits me as I walk into the wooden hut. Sitting comfortably with his feet up on the desk, a friendly looking bloke wearing thick-rimmed glasses grins into his newspaper.

Chris walks up to the desk. 'Excuse me.'

Scratching his Grizzly Adams style beard, the ranger looks up slowly in our direction and smiles, still deep in thought over the article he's reading.

He snaps out of his trance and whips his legs off the desk. 'Sorry, guys. How can I help you?'

Providing him with an overview of the level of trekking we're capable of, he shows us a map of the area pinned to his wall and points out various trails that we can take around the mountain. He also informs us that climbing Mount Rainer itself is out of the question, as it can be dangerous and involves using ice axes and crampons – which funnily enough, we know nothing about.

'So, you suggest we stick to the trails around this area?' Chris asks, pointing to a couple of dotted lines on the map.'

'Absolutely,' he nods. 'Especially the Sunrise trail starting here at White River. It takes you through beautiful meadows, deep forests and leads right to a glacier basin.'

'That sounds fantastic,' he grins. 'Thanks for your help.'

'Sure thing.'

We turn to leave, but Chris hesitates before opening the door. 'Is it possible to pay for a night in the campsite?'

'No can do, buddy. We're all full today. You can try at the Carbon River entrance point.'

'How far is that?'

'About ten miles, or so.'

'OK. Thanks for your help,' I chip in, wanting to have made some contribution.

'No problem,' he smiles, swinging his legs back onto the desk. 'Remember to keep your food locked up from the grizzlies.'

Standing outside, Chris turns to me with a look of fear and excitement in his eyes. 'Did he just say grizzlies?'

'Yeah, I think he did.'

'Excellent!'

Parking the van next to the ranger's office, I take a walk to suss out the toilet facilities. It's our third day without washing since we left Seattle and, although Chris seems content with just spraying on some deodorant in the morning, scratching his head and starting his day, I can feel a pain in the corner of my eye and know it's the beginning of an infection.

Heading across the car park with a towel and a bag of toiletries, I step over a rotten tree trunk and stop in my tracks as a chipmunk dashes out in front of me. It stares boldly in my direction and then darts off again as quickly as it appeared, taunting me with its tail. Refusing to be intimidated by a rodent with attitude, I continue to follow a trail that leads through a cluster of tall pine trees, and reaching a toilet block I circle its perimeter and peer cautiously inside. Gasping, the pungent smell of stale urine and decomposing faeces nearly strikes me to the ground, but regaining my sight I take a deep breath, clench my teeth and head once more into the darkness. The toilet consists of little more than a metallic bowl sunk into the dirt over a twelve-foot hole in the ground. Standing at a safe distance from the rim I expose my tackle to the wall, pause for a moment as I struggle to relax, and then release my bladder in an impressive stream, attacking the dozens of stools hanging out together in the pit below.

Storming back towards the van with an incriminating wet patch, I explain the toilet situation to Chris and he reminds me that we're in the middle of a forest and far from the home comforts of a motel.

'We've got to wash occasionally.'

'Why? It's not like there're any girls around here to impress.'

'But that's not the point, you stinker - its unhygienic!'

'Look, Si. We're supposed to be roughing it, *surviving* in the wilderness and being at one with nature. I mean, can you imagine Ray Mears worrying about smelling like a dead rat?'

'Ray Mears?'

'You must know who Ray Mears is?'

'No.'

Chris shakes his head in disgust. 'He's the survival expert. Everyone knows who Ray Mears is. He's that brilliant Boy Scout who made it onto the telly.'

'Well, if he's a Boy Scout I'm sure he takes great pride in staying clean wherever he is. He would see it as his duty to remain hygienic and maintain his self-respect. It's all part of the code.'

'Yeah, but...'

'Hang on a minute!'

'What?'

'Listen ... can you hear rushing water?'

Pushing Chris towards the trees, we slide down a steep bank, fight through a jungle of thick bushes, climb over huge rocks, and eventually reach a torrent of white water gliding past us like a giant conveyor belt.

'Bloody hell!' I yell, shielding my eyes from the sun. 'Now that's what I call a river!'

'Yeah. It must be White River!'

Looking upstream, the snow capped peak of Mount Rainer towers magnificently above us, and walking over the smooth dry pebbles of an exposed part of the river-bed, we reach a small stream that branches sharply away from the main body of the river.

'Maybe we should wash in this?' I suggest.

'No way! It'll be freezing.'

'You pussy! You're not much of a survival expert now, are you?'

'What...?'

'Well, this is the kind of place where survival experts wash their asses.'

Stripping down to my boxer shorts, I step into the icy cold water and begin to splash my head and face. I feel a sharp pain at my temple, like eating ice cream too quickly, and leap out onto the nearest rock, shaking uncontrollably until the sensation fades.

'OK! Let's see who you're calling a pussy, shall we?' Chris yells.

Wrestling to pull his T-shirt over his head, he competitively takes things one step further and lies down in the flow of the stream. 'AAAHH! *IT'S F-F-FUCKING F-F-FREEZING!*'

'*SOD IT!*' I cry, and turning away, I pull down my shorts and sit testicles first on the soft silt riverbed.

Skipping back to the van as hungry as wolves, we crack open a few beers in celebration of our arrival in the wilderness, and decide to cook up a few of those delicious looking sausages from the supermarket in Everett. Unfortunately, we purchased the wrong type of gas canister for our cooker - well, eight of the bastards to be precise, so we're forced to settle for a big bag of nuts, two cans of tuna and six surprisingly delicious cold meatball sandwiches.

* * *

A bleeping sound from Si's watch wakes me with a start, and through half-closed eyes I look out across an early morning mist hovering above the tree line. There's a sour taste in my mouth and smacking my lips together I sit up, pull my sleeping bag tightly around my neck and stretch my legs out across the backseat.

I see Si curled up in the foetal position on the carpet of the van, and from his rapid eye movements I predict that he's having one of his surreal 'fear dreams', about being trapped in his life - unable to escape the misery. Deciding to let him sleep for a while longer, I slip on a jacket and slide open the door as quietly as possible. Fresh, clean air fills my lungs as I glance across the silent car park. A hacking cough attracts my attention, and I watch a grumpy looking man fall out of his camper van and march off through the trees grasping a toilet roll.

With the day so alive all around me I feel a sudden urge to get moving, but Si's still fast asleep. Under normal circumstances I would never rush a person to get up in the morning, but I start to feel frustrated that we're missing the best part of the day so I grab hold of the van door and slam it in his face.

'*WAKEY*! *WAKEY*! *RISE AND SHINE*!'

Si's confused face peers out of the window, his long hair sticking up wildly and a deep crease running down the side of his cheek. He doesn't move for a few seconds, just darts glances around the car park as he tries to work out not only where he is, but also who he is.

'What time is it?' he croaks, using all of his energy to slide open the window.

'Time we went a-hiking, mate. It's a *beautiful* morning! Let's head off so we can be the first ones on the trail.'

'Give us a chance. I've only just woken up.'

'Come on! Arriba! Arriba! "For nothing can seem foul for those that win".'

He frowns. 'You what?'

'It's Shakespeare.'

'Oh. I thought you were quoting Ray Mears again.'

'No … although, he would be extremely disappointed if he saw you now.'

Rubbing his face Si stretches his arms above his head and lets out a yawn. 'To be honest with you, Chris. I couldn't give a fuck about Ray Mears, or Shakespeare. Just give me a few minutes to wake up and I'll be ready.'

Waiting twenty minutes for Si to have a full body wash, we eventually head off in search of the Sunrise trail, and before long we reach the starting point and a sign warning of bears ahead.

'Here we go,' I beam. 'Now, this is where it gets interesting.'

'Fuck that shit!' Si cries, and storming off in the opposite direction he starts rummaging through the undergrowth, only to reappear with a huge grin on his face and clutching a stick that's about four foot in length and as sharp as a sword.

'Look at this baby! I'm taking *no* chances!'

I glance back at the sign. 'A sensible precaution seeing as the end is nigh.'

'You think so?' he grins, admiring his new weapon.

'Yep. This could be our last few steps on planet earth.'

'Shit, what a downer - I haven't had a threesome yet.'

'Simon, I guess some things in life are just not meant to be. Thanks for being my twin brother, mate. It's been great knowing you.' I reach out and grab hold of his shoulder. 'I still think you're a prick, but if something terrible happens to me out there today, I want you to have my Raleigh Winner racing bike in the shed and my secret stash of jazz mags under my bed.'

Si frowns. 'Jazz mags?'

'Yeah. You know. Top shelf material.'

'Oh, right, cheers. Uh … yeah, I really appreciate that. Well, it's been great knowing you too. If something terrible happens to me today, I want you to have my electric guitar in my bedroom and my Smiths CD's in the shoebox under my stereo.'

Shaking hands, we turn and face the winding trail and with our heads held high, we enter bear country.

After an hour or so, we begin to relax and stop hearing noises and seeing shapes moving between the trees.

'What were we worrying about? The bears are probably more scared of us than we are of them.'

'Do you reckon?'

'Definitely.'

Turning a sharp bend, I spot something on the track and crouch down to take a closer look.

'Bloody hell!'

'What is it?' Si replies, squatting beside me.

'I think it's bear fur and droppings.'

'Piss off!'

'I'm serious! And if I'm not mistaken, that's the faint outline of a paw print.'

Examining the evidence, Si takes a clump of the brown wiry hair and rubs it gently between his fingers. 'Why the fuck didn't we buy some bells? I mean, look at the size of that paw print - it's *huge!*'

'It's like the old dear said, what use is a bell if a thousand pound grizzly is charging you?'

'That's not the point!'

'Yes it is! The bear's not going to be paralysed by fear and run off terrified by the sound of intense clanging, is it?'

'It might.'

'Get real. Do you know anything about bears?'

Si shakes his head. 'No.'

'Have you read those leaflets you picked up from the rangers station yesterday?'

'Uh ... no.'

'Well, you're in deep shit!'

'*Me*? You're just as likely to be eaten, too! Oh, no ... sorry, my mistake. You won't - because you've read a *PISSING LEAFLET*!'

'Keep your mullet on! It's important stuff to know.'

'I know - that's why I picked them up!'

'So why haven't you read them?'

'I haven't had the ... piss off! I don't need to explain myself to you.'

'Let's just calm down. We're panicking over nothing. It's probably weeks old,' I mutter, busy scanning the ground for another stick.

'It looks pretty fresh to me.'

'It can't be! The fur is too wiry and the shit is dry and crumbly.'

'Sort it out, Chris. This is serious. What the fuck do you know? We could be minutes away from being attacked by a vicious monster with sharp teeth. We've been incredibly naïve!'

'Don't be ridiculous! Anyway, all you've talked about until now is how you're dying to see one.'

'Yeah, but now I'm actually here, I'm finding all of this quite unnerving.'

'Look, here's some advice,' I whisper. 'Apparently, if a

bear charges you, all you have to do is stand absolutely
still and avoid eye contact.'

Si stares at me, incredulous. 'Aren't you even a bit
scared?'

'Nah…'

* * *

Chris strides on in front, while I hang back with my
stick poised and ready, secretly pretending it's an automatic rifle. Little blue and yellow flowers poke between
blades of lush green grass, clumsy bumblebees zoom
past fragile butterflies in the mid-morning sunshine,
and remembering that it's often the person at the back
that gets it first, I quicken my pace.

Reaching the mouth of the glacier basin at the source
of White River, we stomp across rocks in our heavy
boots just beneath the snowline. A large frog plunges
into a rock pool and we sit down by a small waterfall,
watching the river twist and turn into the valley below.

'This place is amazing,' Chris smiles, taking a large
gulp of water. 'It's like prehistoric earth or something.'

'Yeah. It's beautiful. Certainly beats being at work.'

Chris shivers. 'Ooh … what a horrible thought. What
time do you reckon it is back home?'

'About two in the afternoon, I think. I would have just
finished lunch and be on the way back to my desk for
an afternoon of emailing friends, coffees in the canteen
and regular cigarette breaks.'

'Is that really what you did all day?'

'Pretty much,' I nod, biting into a bruised apple.

'Fucking hell, Si. Easy life!'

'*Easy life*? My life was hell. No. It was worse than hell.'

'Sitting in an air-conditioned office all day, surrounded

59

by sexy office chicks is not worse than hell.'

I pause before taking another bite. 'And there goes a man who has *no* concept of the absolute, bollock-numbing tedium of office life.'

'Yeah. Well, it's all relative, isn't it? I mean, try working down a fucking coal mine and see how you feel?'

'Like you'd know! Don't you remember all the *shit* I had to go through with that wanker Lawrence Cox?'

'Was he the prick who'd leave an old red coat on the back of his chair to look like he was always in the office?'

'Did I tell you about that?'

'You were taking the piss out of him one night in the pub. Didn't you tell him to go fuck himself?'

'I can't believe I did that. I'd only been working there a few weeks.'

* 'The guy sounded like he deserved it.'

'He did. I suppose it would have been all right if he'd remained some interfering little twat from another department, instead three days later becoming my boss!'

'Whoops.'

'He made the next six months of my life hell.'

'Office politics, Si. What a load of bollocks.'

'Bully boys are everywhere in the corporate jungle.'

'Why didn't you leave, you idiot?'

'No way! It was my lucky break - my first step into journalism. I wasn't going to be beaten by some oily little weasel.'

'But how could you be arsed to put up with that shit?'

'I must have thought I had too. I remember a tutor at college saying "you should *always* stay in your first job for at least two years".'

Chris frowns. 'Two years? Even if you hate it? 'I gues-looks good on your CV.'

'So what happened? Did he leave?'

'No, I applied for a job on another channel. Although,

that was around the time I started to spend my days emailing friends and taking cigarette breaks every five minutes.'

I don't know what I hated more about my career in the internet, the office politics between middle managers scuffling for position - or the absolute tedium of being trapped all day between the same four walls. My time there seemed such a waste of a life, producing content that I knew few people would actually read, and which lay trapped behind a soulless glass screen. I felt a burning desire to create something real, something tangible, and would often daydream of jacking it all in to become a carpenter or a boat builder. Landing a promotion to become producer of the live celebrity interviews, relieved the boredom for a couple of years after graduating from the news desk, but hours of listening to half-baked pop and soap stars drone on about their shallow existences, eventually ground me down again. I also found myself feeling envious of the authors and film directors who were pushing boundaries and pursuing their dreams. I desperately wanted to do something myself, but I hadn't the confidence or the direction to know where to even begin. Whilst I was going out with Emily, jacking it all in never seemed an option. In a city where who you are and what you do mean everything, I was well and truly sucked in, and tossing all that aside has been a liberating experience I never thought I'd feel again.

The journey back down the mountain is fast as we bound past streams and stumble through dark forests. Less concerned about being eaten by a bear, I begin to feel disappointed that we haven't seen one. Turning a corner, we acknowledge a middle-aged couple making their way up the path.

'Is it much further to the top?' the lady puffs, struggling to catch her breath.

'Not far now,' I reply. 'About another forty minutes, or so.'

'Forty minutes? That's *great* news! Tony, did you hear that? It's about forty minutes to the top.'

Turning to the gentleman stood beside her, I notice that he's blind.

'Mary!' he cries. 'Ask him if he's seen a bear.'

'Have you?' she asks with a smile.

'Not yet, but we saw droppings and fur about a mile up the path.'

'Did you hear that, Tony? They saw droppings and fur about a mile up the path.'

'Can I touch a glacier?' the guy beams, hope radiating from his vacant eyes.

Chris shakes his head. 'No, I'm afraid you can't. But there's a beautiful view from up there.'

Tony's face falls. 'Oh.'

Shocked by Chris's insensitive words, the woman silently leads her husband away.

'You fucking idiot!' I cry, watching them shuffle off around the corner.

'What?'

'That man was blind, you fool!'

'Was he?'

'Yes.'

'Well, how was I supposed to know?'

'It was obvious!'

'Was it?'

'*Yes*! I mean, what did you think was wrong with him?'

'I didn't think there was anything "wrong" with him. I'm not the kind of person who takes the piss out of people with disabilities, OK? I just thought he was a bit weird that's all.'

Meeting the Locals

Si turns the key but nothing happens. He turns it again, and nothing. He tries for a third time, madly pumping on the accelerator and churning the starter motor over and over. I sit next to him, pressing an imaginary pedal and turning an imaginary key, mimicking his every move.

'Bollocks!' I groan, slapping the dashboard. 'We've bought a pile of crap!'

'Chill out! Maybe the battery's flat,' Si replies, turning the key one more time.

'It can't be.'

'Why not? We're always leaving the interior light on.'

'Well, what the fuck are we going to do now?'

'We're going to jump start the engine!'

Leaving the van Si walks purposefully over to a car parked opposite, and within a matter of seconds the bonnet is up and a rather creepy looking guy in full trekking gear works enthusiastically to connect our battery to his.

'OK. Strike her up!' he shouts, poking his head into view.

Si turns the key. Again nothing happens. Our new

friend dives back under the bonnet and fiddles around with the leads.

'Well, guys. I just don't understand why it's not holding any charge. I've had these jump leads for years and they work just fine for me.'

I look over at him and then at the miserable old woman sat in the back of his car.

'I'll tell you what,' he continues. 'Let's leave it charging for a while, so my mom and me can have something to eat on those benches over there. I know what it's like to be stranded - it's not a problem for me, or my mom!' he grins, waving maniacally in the direction of the old prune.

'Thanks ever so much,' Si smiles. 'What's your name by the way?'

'Tim. Tim Sharp,' he boasts, slapping the back of his head as he waddles over to a nearby picnic table.

'What the fuck was all that about?' I mutter.

Si turns to me and frowns. 'What do you mean? He seems like a really nice bloke – a bit odd, but very helpful if you ask me.'

'Shut up ... he's *mad*! I mean, what was all that slapping his head business? That ain't normal.'

'Fucking hell, Chris. Here we go!'

'What?'

'You think he's a serial killer, don't you?'

'Well, I wouldn't go that far. Although, *actually*! Yes, you're right. I think he's a fucking serial killer!'

'You're kidding me? The poor guy's just out trekking with his mother, for Christ's sake!'

'Exactly! And has it occurred to you that she can hardly walk, let alone spend the day hiking up a mountain.'

'She's probably just come along for the ride.'

'*Ah-ha*! That's it! She waits in the car while he goes into the woods alone and buries his latest victim. It's the perfect cover.'

'Shut up! I *can't* believe the crap that goes through your mind.'

'OK, then. If it makes you feel better he's just a very kind, helpful person - whatever you say, Si.'

Reclining in my seat I glance over at the picnic table to spy on what they're up to, but jump in surprise as I see Tim starring motionless at me through the open window.

'JESUS CHRIST!'

'What's the matter?' he asks, the tone of his voice sounding somehow deeper than before.

'Nothing. You just surprised me, that's all.'

'Did I? Sorry about that - just thought I'd let you know that my food was yummy and has gone inside my tummy,' he smirks rubbing his stomach.

'Oh ... uh ... OK,' I smile, jabbing my elbow into Si's shoulder. 'Wake up! Tim's back to help us with the battery.'

Si opens his eyes and we both watch as Tim skips over to the two engines.

'FIRE AWAY, GUYS!' Tim yells, with far too much enthusiasm.

Si turns the ignition and the van jumps into life.

'YES!' I shout over the roar of the engine. *'WE'RE BACK ON THE ROAD!'*

'Goodbye Rainer,' Si laughs, 'see you again someday.'

Disconnecting the leads, Tim slams the bonnet shut and, after a few quick slaps to the back of his head, he rushes over with a smile.

'I'm the winner!' he bows. 'Thank you! Thank you!'

'No.' Si applauds. 'Thank you!'

'No problem, guys. I *really* enjoyed myself.'

'Well, you take care now, Tim!' I call, as we pull away.

'I will ... you can be sure of that.'

With a farewell of manic waving from Tim, we turn

onto the road and head off through the forest.

'OK. You were right,' Si laughs, as we disappear out of sight. 'He's definitely a serial killer.'

* * *

It feels good to be behind the wheel again. Chris studies the map as shadows swirl inside the van, and gliding through a winding corridor of trees we're guided almost hypnotically along the highway.

The views are breathtaking as we head for the volcanic Mount St Helens, and as we slowly make our descent through the Cascades, the highway begins to level out and the forests disappear. The grass on the rolling hills to our left is suddenly dry and yellow like straw, and as we pass vast meadows filled with grazing horses, I pull over and buy a bag of fresh cherries from the roadside. With stained lips, we chase Snake River to the banks of the magnificent Lake Rimrock, and inspired by its incredible beauty we decide to park up for the night.

Chris peers over his shades and points at a lay-by up ahead. 'How about under those trees? But not too close to that RV over there.'

'Roger, Captain,' I reply, swerving off the road. 'Fasten your seat belts, we're coming into land.'

Bouncing uncontrollably over uneven ground, we skid dangerously to a halt beneath an enormous evergreen tree.

'Thank you for flying with Raven Airlines, it's been a real pleasure. Yo'll come back now.'

Unimpressed with my flying skills, Chris grabs his binoculars from the glove box and scans the horizon.

'What can you see?' I ask, squinting out across the water.

'Osprey I think, and shit loads of them.'

Trying to focus on the blurred dots circling above the mountains on the far side of the lake, I'm unable to see anything in great detail and quickly loose interest. I'm suddenly distracted by a middle-aged man wearing blue Speedo's, stood outside the RV.

'Look at that dude over there,' I whisper, nodding vigorously in the guys direction.

Lowering his binoculars Chris glances over. 'Wow! Fat bastard!'

Stood with his hands on his hips and his belly pointing out across the lake, he watches a speedboat dragging a water skier around a small island.

'It must be great being that age,' I smile, patting my stomach.

Chris frowns. 'Do you think so?'

'Yeah. Look at him. He's wearing fucking Speedo's, for Christ's sake. The only time in your life you can respectfully get away with wearing those, is after you've got married and had kids. I suppose, why shouldn't he stand there and scratch his hairy gut in public? He's a man of the world - he deserves *respect*! He's not out to impress the ladies, he doesn't give a shit what people think about him.'

'Either that or he's just given up,' Chris replies, lifting up his T-shirt and examining his stomach.

'Whatever it is, he's certainly not ashamed of promoting his inadequacies by wearing that swimming attire.'

'Very true. I'll look forward to the day!'

Chris returns to scanning the horizon, while I grab a towel and walk over to a steep slope leading down to the water. I peer over the edge and decide to have a swim. Pulling on my walking boots for extra grip, I send a foot over the side and test the ground for stability.

'Careful, Si! You're gonna kill yourself.'

'I'll be all right,' I gasp, straining to support my weight as I lower myself down.

'You don't look all right.'

'Have faith. It's all about taking your time and ensuring you have a good … *F-F-FUUUCK*!'

Feeling the dry bank crumble beneath me, I lose my balance and in true Norman Wisdom style, I tumble headfirst into the lake along with a ton of shale.

'*YOU FUCKING IDIOT*!' Chris yells, peering down at me below. 'Are you OK?'

'*HOLY SHIT! DID YOU SEE THAT*?'

Further along the bank, our fat neighbour looks down in mild amusement. I throw him a wave and start kicking my legs to stay afloat.

'Come on in, Chris! The waters beautiful!'

Finding an easier route down, Chris attempts to catch fish with a stick, a slice of ham and a safety pin, but swiftly abandons his plan and tucks into a can of BBQ flavoured Pringles.

'You seem a bit more chilled these days,' he mumbles, forcing a large stack of the snacks into his mouth.

'What do you mean by that?' I frown, laying my wet T-shirt on a rock.

'Come off it! You know exactly what I mean. If you'd fallen into a lake with all of your clothes on a few days ago - you would have been *well* pissed off.'

'I know. Isn't it great!'

Chris turns to me with a smile.

'What?'

'Nothing. It's good to have you back, Si. It's good to have you back.'

* * *

Grabbing my camera, I position Si with his back against the magnificent Mount St Helens Volcano, which looms eerily behind less than five miles away.

'OK. Say cheese!'

'*CHEESE...*' he grins falsely, squinting in the bright sunlight.

A large group of tourists wait to pass by. I pause sadistically a moment longer than necessary and wait for his reaction.

'For fuck's sake, Chris. *Hurry up!*'

'Hold on! Don't move a muscle. I'm trying to get the composition right.'

'Forget the composition! Just take the bloody picture!'

'OK, OK. I've taken it.'

Dropping his smile, Si marches over to me.

'What the hell do you think you're doing?' he snaps, watching the amused tourists file by. 'That was so embarrassing. I looked like a right prat.'

'It was a joke ... I'm sorry.'

'Well, it wasn't very funny. I can't believe you call yourself a photographer. *You're crap!*'

'No I'm not. I just like to take my time.'

Leaving the main observation point, Si drives back down the tight mountainous roads and through the black charred landscape, until we reach a dirt track leading into a forest. Parking up in a clearing well away from the main road, Si grabs the pots and pans from the back of the van, while I wander off in search of firewood.

Considering the last time we built a fire was when we were thirteen, which didn't involve wood at all, but an old builders jacket and a shit load of paraffin, it isn't long before we're watching roaring flames lick the cool evening air.

'It's a bit creepy here, isn't it?' Si whispers, as he pours water into a saucepan.

I dart my eyes around the clearing. 'Yeah. A little.'

Removing two plastic beakers from a faded Tescos carrier bag, Si looks up and smiles. 'Fancy a brew?'

'Yes, please. I'm parched.'

'It might take a while.'

'You take your time. I'll start with a beer.'

Leaning back against the van, I enjoy the silence until I hear something from deep within the forest.

'Si, stop what you're doing a minute.'

'Why?'

'Just listen! Can you hear it?'

With his mouth open wide, he listens intently. 'Hear what?'

'An Elk.'

'An *Elk*? What's an Elk?'

'You don't know what an Elk is?'

He shakes his head. 'Nope.'

'There it is again! Did you hear it?'

'Yeah! What's it called again?'

'It's an Elk.'

'Is it like a giant elf?'

'You're joking, right?'

'Yeah. Of course I am. But what is it?'

'It's a cross between a deer and a moose. A big horse-sized creature with antlers.'

'Sounds bizarre.'

'I guess it is. Hey, did you know that over a million and a half animals and birds were killed around here when Mount St Helens erupted.'

'*A million and a half?*'

'Yep. Over two hundred and fifty square miles, or something, were completely destroyed. It turned all the trees into burnt matchsticks. It's crazy when you think about it. All the animals were just wiped out. Even the poor fish were boiled alive in the rivers.'

'Fucking hell, that's one mother of an explosion.'

'It was huge! Some of the ash even landed in New York. You could see the mushroom cloud from space!'

'Didn't some old bloke get killed in the explosion?'

'Yeah, he refused to move when they evacuated the area.'

'What happened to him?'

'I dunno, but I guess that by the time it was all over he had quite a lot on his mind.'

It's late in the evening and the fire is still alive. Feeling well fed and content, I crack open another beer, but just as I'm about to take a good old gulp, I hear the faint sound of a motorbike making its way up the track.

'Shit. I hope it's not a ranger,' Si whispers, looking at his can of beer and then at the fire.

A moped carrying two people appears in full view and pulls up beside the van. A stocky guy wearing a bright red helmet and leather gloves dismounts, followed by a young woman in a flowery dress.

'Hi,' he smiles, 'beautiful evening.'

'Sure is,' I reply.

Removing her helmet, the young woman avoids eye contact.

'Great evening for a walk,' the guy laughs nervously, clutching a blanket in his arms.

We watch them back away and disappear into the woods.

'A walk my arse,' I slur, 'who are they trying to kid? They're going to have sex!'

'*Really*?' Si cries, sounding surprised. 'But they looked like father and daughter. They're probably just looking at the creatures in the forest.'

'Ha! Yeah, right. The only forest creature she'll see tonight is a one-eyed trouser snake.'

'Lucky git! She was *really* pretty. How did he manage

to pull her?'

'Fuck knows. I bet his wife wouldn't be too happy if she found out.'

Si frowns. 'His *wife*?'

'Uh-huh. She probably hasn't got a clue what he's getting up to.'

'How do you know he's married?'

'Why else would he be sneaking about in the woods with a young woman? And his body language said it all. Unless, of course, it's the woman who's having the affair.'

Si shakes his head. 'Nah.'

'Why not?'

'She didn't look the type to have an affair.'

'The type?'

'Yeah, she looked *too* nice.'

'Bollocks! What's nice got to do with anything? It's often the quiet, innocent women who are the darkest.'

'*Really*?'

'You can guarantee it. Maybe they're both having an affair?'

'Ah, the plot thickens!'

'That's it! They're both married and they're both getting some on the side. Maybe he's her teacher?' I grin devilishly.

'Well, if that's the case,' Si growls. 'It looks like she's about to receive her first biology lesson!'

'Cheating!' I cry.

'Deceit!'

'*SLEAZE*!'

Hells Canyon

Chris is keen to push onto Hells Canyon, so we leave Washington State and head towards the Columbia River, driving along part of the Lewis and Clark scenic highway.

Exploring west from the Mississippi to the Pacific, Meriwether Lewis and William Clark set out in 1804 with their *Corps of Discovery*. Their mission was to find a Northwest passage across the United States, and on May 21st they led a group of men up the Missouri River making great discoveries along the way. Attacked by grizzly bears and battling against the treacherous rivers and unforgiving wilderness, they made it all the way to the Pacific Ocean and back - some eight thousand miles in twenty-eight months. They returned home heroes, hailed as famous explorers and legends in their own lifetimes.

Sat in the comfort and safety of our van, I try to imagine what it must have been like to travel along the river for thousands of miles into the unknown. I cannot compare our journey to the one Lewis and Clark embarked on, but as we leave our old lives in London further and further behind, we too are unsure of what lies ahead and I begin to understand how they might have felt.

Wind surfers bob seal-like in the midday sun as we cross into the state of Oregon over a flimsy looking bridge at Hood River, and then stop for gas in the ugly industrial township of The Dalles. I'm greeted by a friendly "howdy" in a nearby gas station, but feel no great desire to stick around, so we continue on our merry way - loving the road.

Stretching out across the back seat, I watch a deep red sun drop below the horizon and paint flames across the sky. Vast open spaces of dry grassland spread out into the distance across the Columbia Plateau, and as night falls we pull over into a rest area on top of a hill and sleep peacefully until daylight.

The following morning we approach Riggins, a small town that sits in the shadow of the He Devil Mountain range, and feel ready to get out there on foot and climb to the Hells Canyon Dam, the deepest gorge in North America. The chance of seeing a mountain lion has Chris foaming at the mouth, and hanging a sharp left on the outskirts of town, we begin to climb a serious hill.

Flooring the van for the first few miles, I shout words of encouragement over the noise of the engine.

'It seems to be stuck in first gear!' Chris yells, as we jerk between bursts of acceleration.

'Ease off the accelerator!'

Checking to see if there's anyone behind, I suddenly notice thick black smoke pouring into the air from behind the van.

'*SHIT! PULL OVER, CHRIS!*'

'You what?'

'*THERE'S SMOKE!*'

'Where?'

'*JUST PULL OVER!*'

He slams on the brakes. We both jump out and run around to the back of the van. With arms folded, we look in disbelief at the long trail of smoke snaking off down the hillside.

'*BOLLOCKS*!' Chris yells, kicking the back wheel. '*BOLLOCKS, BASTARD, PILE OF SHIT*!'

'Chill out!'

'Well, it's *fucked*, isn't it!'

'Not necessarily! And there's no need to shout at it like that- it's bad karma.'

'Bad karma? It's a pissing van, Si.'

'So. You're tempting fate.'

'*FATE*? You superstitious twat.'

'Shut up.'

'You know what you can do with your fate bullshit, don't you?'

'Chris...'

'You can stick it up your arse!'

Rolling uncontrollably back down the mountain, Chris narrowly avoids a gatepost as he steers aggressively over a cattle grid.

'Slow down! We nearly crashed then.'

'Who cares! It's fucked anyway. I thought that tossing mechanic was a bit quick to knock the price down. He knew it was a pile of shite, so he flogged it to a couple of dumb-ass tourists.'

'You don't know that for sure. Let's just take our time and find out what the problem is.'

Ditching the van in a gateway to a field, Chris puffs anxiously on a cigarette as the traffic roars past us on the main road.

Drawing on my own cigarette, I try to seek solace in our time of misery. 'Put it this way, we could have broken down miles from anywhere, which would have been *really* bad.'

'Shut up, Si.'

Silence. Just the roar of the traffic and heavy breathing as we smoke ourselves into oblivion.

'So, what are we gonna do now?'

Chris shrugs a "fuck knows".

'Its getting dark. Maybe we should stay here for the night and find a garage in Riggins tomorrow?'

'Whatever, mate ... I'm past caring.'

'Come on! This is where the trip gets interesting. You wanted an adventure, well ... this is it!'

Chris reaches over and stubs his cigarette out in the ashtray. 'I'd hardly call sitting in a broken down van on a busy main road, an adventure!'

'Well, you're just going to have to deal with it. It's survival time. We can either sink or swim.'

'Sink or swim? Either way it's out of our control.'

Chris's childish mood dampens mine, and I begin to wonder if he might be right. Maybe we have bought a pile of crap. Maybe our trip is over before it has even begun.

Tossing and turning in my sleeping bag, I dream about London. Characters from my former life haunt me like demons, and I find myself running between the floors of the office building where I worked in Fulham. It's late, and everywhere I go, the huge open plan rooms are empty. Waves of computer monitors loom from every direction and surreal images of my ex-girlfriend Emily, in various seductive poses, spin on their screen savers.

Racing up the stairs, I enter a door on the third floor. I weave between the spinning desks, but suddenly freeze. Light spills out from under the door to the boardroom. I can hear the sound of a girl giggling in my head, and I walk in slow motion towards the door - hesitating before turning the handle and peering in. Gasping, my heart explodes as I see Emily through the gloom of the candle lit room, her naked back arched as she straddles a man across the boardroom table. Looking over her shoulder she begins to laugh maniacally at me, the expression on her face filling me with despair and rage. I reach inside my jacket and pull out a revolver. I shakily aim it at her head, but she doesn't react, she just continues to taunt me as she laughs and grinds above the man between her legs. *"WHY ARE YOU DOING THIS TO ME?"* I scream, impulsively pulling the trigger. Stumbling back I watch in horror as a pathetic dribble of water squirts out of the barrel of the pistol. Emily points in my direction and continues to cackle mockingly.

"WHO IS HE? WHO THE FUCK IS HE?"

Feeling the room begin to spin, I turn and feel a sharp pain in my chest as I see an old red coat hanging from the back of a boardroom chair. "No. Please. No." I whimper. Releasing the water pistol from my grasp, I watch as it falls in slow motion to the floor. Feeling helpless, I turn to my right and hurl myself over to the emergency exit door that leads out onto a roof terrace. Slamming the door open, I fall towards the railings, and I already know it's too late. It's over. Looking over my shoulder my ex-boss Lawrence Cox, is stood naked in the doorway, grinning from ear-to-ear with my water pistol in his hand. "See you in hell," he hisses, and with a mighty roar of laughter he blasts a powerful jet into my face like a water cannon. Knocking me off balance, I topple backwards over the railings. My body twists and turns as I fall to my doom.

* * *

I wake with the sudden urge to take a shit. Stepping over Si, panic fills my eyes as I reach frantically for the toilet roll on the front seat, and I very nearly follow through as I'm suddenly disturbed by a face at the window.

'Got a problem?' the rugged looking guy calls through the gap in the window.

'I'm sorry ... what was that?' I reply, studying the shiny red boil on the tip of his nose.

'Do you have a problem?'

'Uh...'

'...Yes!' Si calls to my rescue. 'We've broken down, I'm afraid.'

The guy nods, unashamedly picking his nose and eating it. 'You want me to take a look?'

Gritting my teeth I glance down at the toilet roll, unsure what to do.

'That would be great,' Si replies.

As they peer under the bonnet I make a dash for the nearest field, returning seconds later and a few pounds lighter.

'Hmm...' the guy nods, studying the dipstick.

We both look at him with keen interest.

'No...' he tuts, sliding it back into place.

For the next five minutes, we're kept on tenterhooks as we wait for his diagnosis.

'Hold on a darn minute,' he spits, getting down on his hands and knees and peering under the van. 'It's your transmission fluid!'

Si scratches his head. 'Shit. What does that mean?'

'Well, kid,' he replies, wiping his fingers on his grease stained jeans. 'You haven't got any! If you look back at the road there, you'll see it's all leaked out. I can give you the transmission fluid I've got in the back of my truck - should be enough to get you to a garage, but I'd get it fixed before it gets any worse.'

'How much do you think it'll cost to get it repaired?' I ask.

'If it's what I think it is, you'll need your transmission system totally re-building ... and that ain't gonna be cheap.'

'Say a hundred?'

'Try a thousand.'

'A *thousand*?'

'Yep.'

'Holy shit! Well, thanks for looking at it.'

'Not a problem. Oh … by the way, kid. If Gus caught you crapping in his field like that you'd be out of here with or without your van, so I'd be on your way.'

Grabbing the transmission fluid from his truck, he throws it to Si.

'Be on your way,' he grunts.

Mortified, we stand at the side of the road and pathetically wave him goodbye as he disappears in a cloud of dust.

'He seemed like a nice man,' Si coughs.

'Yeah. Charming,' I reply. 'It can't cost one thousand dollars, can it? He's talking crap!'

'He seemed to know what he was on about.'

'Damn. I knew it would be bad. There's no way that we can afford to spend another grand on this donkey.'

'Well, what we gonna do?'

'Hope it doesn't conk out before we get to LA, I suppose.'

'Chris, I don't think my heart can take much more of this. Maybe we should slow down a bit, ease up on the mileage - it's *not* a fucking race!'

'True … hey! Was that dude a redneck, or what? He looked like the big scary one in that Burt Reynolds movie.'

'What, *Cannonball Run*?' Si grins.

'No. You know. That film with the deformed inbred playing the banjo.'

'*Smokey and the Bandit*?'

'Nope.'

'Uh … *The Littlest Whorehouse in Texas*?'

'Hold on a minute, Si. It's on the tip of my tongue.'

'*Boogie Nights*?'

'No. Keep trying.'

'Chris, I don't know! Give me a clue.'

'How can I give you a clue if I don't know myself?'

'I haven't the foggiest, mate.'

'Ah-ha! I think it begins with D.'

'*Disclosure!*'

I shake my head. 'No. That was Michael Douglas and Demi Moore. Cracking film, though.'

'Yeah … imagine getting your hands on her - '

'*Deliverance*! Thank fuck for that.'

'Oh … *that* Burt Reynolds film! Now, that is a cracking movie. "Squeal like a pig boy! Squeal like a pig".'

'That's the one. "You sure do have a pretty mouth",' I add, in a crap Hillbilly accent.

'What a classic. Although, don't two blokes fall prey to rednecks and get fucked up the ass?'

'Yeah. That's it.'

We both stop laughing and fall silent.

'Shall we go, then?' I mutter, sprinting round to the driver's door.

'Good idea!'

Love & the Dole

Heading for the cowboy town of Missoula, Chris spies a liquor store and we decide to grab a bottle of the hard stuff to celebrate the fact we've still got wheels.

Standing on the pavement outside, I notice that all of the windows along the front of the store are blacked out. A bell rings as we enter, and a surprised shop assistant jerks her head in our direction. Politely greeting the sour faced woman, we make our way inside and look around in awe at the shelves stacked high from floor to ceiling with bottles of alcohol.

'I think we've come to the right place,' Chris whispers, rubbing his hands together.

The room smells of damp old wood and tobacco, and I clomp around the shop feeling immediately at home. I've always found something comforting about off-licences, and just love the idea of an entire shop dedicated to the purpose of intoxicating its customers.

Scanning over the wines we head for the whiskey section, pause longingly at the single malts, and finally agree on a cheap litre bottle of bourbon called Old Crow. Placing it reverently on the counter, I notice that the eyes of the serving wench are struggling to focus on my face.

'You got any ID?' she slurs, swatting the air at an invisible fly.

'Sure,' I nod, feeling chuffed she's asked and proudly flash her my passport.

Paying for the bottle, she shoos us away with a flick of her wrist, and we emerge blinking from the store with our booze tightly wrapped in brown paper.

'She thought I was under twenty-one,' I laugh, straightening my posture.

'She's *so* wasted she would have asked Granddad for his ID, you ageing hippy.'

'Shut it! I look younger than you, you meathead.'

'Uh … I hate to destroy your illusions, but you lost your boyish good looks way back in the nineties, pal.'

Climbing into the van, I flip down the sun visor and study my face in the mirror.

'No I haven't,' I snap, pressing my swollen pasta-shell eyes. 'I'm still a handsome young man.'

'Si, you're as skinny as a rake and you weigh like a woman!' Chris howls, and striking up the engine we head back on the road.

Entering the state of Montana, it isn't long before we hit the outskirts of Missoula. Rows of Casino lounges and saloon bars line the highway, and it's immediately clear that we've come to the right place.

Turning left at a crossroads, we spot a cheap looking motel comically called 'The Bel Air', and happy with the price we check in for the night. It's the kind of place where someone usually gets murdered or at least hides from the cops, and from the outside it looks like a row of Hi-de-hi holiday camp chalets, with identical blue doors all facing the car park.

Flicking on the TV, we decide to chill out in the room all afternoon and watch a movie on the Disney Channel. Needless-to-say, it ends happily-ever-after and near to the dramatic climax I begin to feel quite emotional as Michael, the rich and pretentious nephew from LA, saves his auntie's cattle ranch in Nebraska from bankruptcy and amends his selfish ways.

Clearing my throat, I jump off the bed and recommend a taste of the whiskey. Chris switches to VH1 and a documentary called "Hell Raisers" about rock icons through the decades. Providing the perfect soundtrack for drinking, I pour two large shots to the sound of 'Light My Fire', and tossing my head back I take a large swig from the bottle.

It was soon after my 14th birthday when I discovered the sound of northern soul. I remember going back to a mate's house one night after hanging out at the town fun fair, and listening to his older brother's Stone Roses album. I was instantly hooked, and buying a pair of 38-inch wide parallel jeans and a hooded top, I grew my hair in the style of an impressive pair of curtains. Meeting at the park every Friday night, we'd drink Thunderbirds cider and smoke JPS cigarettes, and on one occasion scored a spliff's worth and attempted to roll a joint.

Up until this time I hadn't had a real girlfriend, although I had managed to snog a few girls at the odd illicit house party. It wasn't until I was introduced to Kelly Middleton that my eyes were properly opened to their full potential. We went out for a few months, enjoyed a clumsy grope *or* two, but the relationship ended around the time my brand new Adidas Gazelles were snatched from her porch, and after she bought me the sickly sentimental Righteous Brothers cover of the love song, 'Only Time' for Valentines day.

Staying faithful to my music I moved on, and whilst browsing the vinyl section in Spin-a-Disk Records one lazy Saturday afternoon, I bumped into a lad I knew from school. It turned out his music tastes were similar to mine, and after a challenging conversation about obscure Indie bands and NME, we agreed to go and see Nirvana play live at the Hummingbird in Birmingham. This was the start of a beautiful friendship and nearly every weekend we'd see bands, mosh, get fucked, throw-up and fall hopelessly in love with older chicks from afar.

At this time it seemed clear to me that music was my life, and soon after starting my A-levels I was offered an opportunity that only seemed to confirm my destiny. I was asked to be the front man in a band called 'The Blood Sucking Flower Fairies'. Overnight, I was transformed into a Rock God. Despite shitting my pants every time we scored a gig, I was in my element for the next couple of years as we jammed for hours in a dirty little studio, smoking weed and writing songs. It felt like we were changing the world, doing something really meaningful with our lives, and everything since has seemed quite dull in comparison.

* * *

Sitting outside a busy steak house on the main street, I begin to feel a little pissed.

'Look at that young couple over there,' I whisper, pointing discreetly in their direction.

Si rests his elbows on the table and leans forward. 'You what?'

'Look at that couple sitting on the bench to our left.'

He takes a quick peep. 'What, the couple dressed like Sonny and Cher?'

'Yeah. How long do you think they've been seeing each other?'

He takes a sip of his beer. 'Uh…'

'Actually, don't tell me. I'll bet it's been about three years.'

'Three years? How can you tell?'

'For a start they've barely said a word to each other in the past half an hour. The two of them are just sitting there in painful silence.'

'Maybe it's a comfortable silence?'

'Don't be silly. Look at the girl, she's bored out of her mind.'

'Not necessarily, she could be tired.'

'Si, it's a well-known fact that most relationships turn sour or end after three years. I saw it on *Oprah*. It's called the three-year-itch. It makes complete sense if you think about it. After three years you either get engaged, married, or you end it. It's the crossroads in a relationship - make or break time.'

Glancing up, I'm interrupted by an attractive waitress peering down at me.

'You guys need anything?'

'Two more beers, please,' I smile.

'Hey … are you guys from England?'

We both nod.

'Wow. I love your accents,' she squeals, swaying shyly from side-to-side. 'Say something!'

'Like what?' I smile.

'I love it! Say something else!'

Feeling embarrassed, I turn to Si whose gaze is fixed firmly on her angel face. I look round at the other tables to make sure no one is listening.

'Uh … cup of tea Arthur … anyone for tennis, chaps? Strawberries and cream, mother,' I mutter in true Hugh Grant style. 'Is that the kind of thing you're after?'

The waitress giggles and skips back into the restaurant.

'Bloody hell, Chris. We should take advantage of this.'

'Definitely!'

Pausing in mid sentence, I look in amazement as a big green monster truck, with flames painted down the sides and tyres the size of a mini metro, suddenly skids into the car park, and roars to a halt outside the restaurant.

A large crowd gathers around and we sit dumbfounded as a young woman in a wedding dress climbs down from the back of the truck, looking rather flushed and incredibly wind swept. A man leaps out of the driver's seat, presumably the groom, and races over to his new wife and they start to dance around the car park laughing hysterically.

'Only in America,' I smile, checking her out.

'No shit!' Si cries, raising his glass. 'But fancy making her ride in the back of his truck while he chills out in the front listening to music.'

'She's probably showing off her wedding dress. Women just love to be the princess for a day.'

When I was at school, a girl in my class got hitched to a bloke over twice her age. Despite having only met him three months before, whilst working as a receptionist in a hotel, they seemed to be genuinely in love; which didn't, of course, prevent anyone from predicting that their relationship was doomed from the start. I was invited to the wedding, held at a large manor house near to our hometown of Daventry in the Midlands. She was the first of my friends foolish enough to take the plunge so I was really looking forward to it.

It turned out to be a great day. The sky was cloudless, the service went without a hitch and all the usual traditions were followed. The groom gave a sincere speech telling his wife how beautiful she looked as she walked down the aisle, despite reading from notes he'd written days before the event. Enormous auntie's danced the Twist with mortified husbands, hoards of seven-year-olds raced through the building terrorising anything in a wheelchair, and the happy couple were whisked away to begin a romantic honeymoon in Antigua.

Unfortunately, the married bliss was to be short-lived - three weeks to be precise. It turned out that a mere six days after returning from their perfect honeymoon the bride caught her caring, loving husband in bed with her mother. As you would expect the bride was devastated, but ironically six months after the divorce she married her ex-husband's best mate and his best man was, *wait for it*, her ex-husband!

'Si, did you know that nearly fifty percent of marriages end in divorce?'

'Don't tell me ... it's the three-year-itch.'

'No, that's for relationships.'

'I thought marriage was a relationship?'

'Yeah, but when you're talking about marriage it's called the seven-year-itch.'

'Three ... seven ... how many itches are there?'

'There aren't anymore. The seven-year-itch is the stage couples reach if they make it past the three-year-itch. Once they've got the house, the designer vacuum cleaner, two cars on the drive and a couple of kids, they're left wondering what the hell to do next.'

'Are you sure you're not getting this confused with the smashing a mirror superstition? That's seven years bad luck.'

'Si, don't be a dick. I'm a bit pissed, but please don't insult my intelligence. No. It's a well known fact, that almost one in three people who have been married for between six and nine years, wish at some point that they could wake up one morning and not be married anymore.'

Si scratches his head and leans back in his seat. 'Really?'

'Yep. And what's more, it's been proven that around

forty-two percent of people within a marriage secretly yearn to go off and travel.'

'*Forty two percent*? That's shit loads!'

'You're telling me. I blame all these marriage disasters on celebrities. Did you know that over thirty percent...'

'Chris! Sorry to interrupt you, but what is it with you and all of these facts? Where do you get this shit from?'

'The fountain of all knowledge, dear boy: *Trisha*, *Kilroy* and *Oprah*, the wisdom of Daytime TV, and who said being on the dole wasn't educational!'

My first real memories of living in London are from the inside of the Streatham dole office. The year before, Si had moved down to the big smoke to start a course in business and media somewhere near Elephant and Castle. Spying an opportunity, I left my job on the local newspaper and moved into a student house with him and a few of his mates from college.

I hadn't really planned what I'd do when I actually got there, and before I'd even unpacked my pants, I found myself with a UB40 in my hand and a guilty conscience hanging over my head; I had signed myself onto the 'rock & roll'.

Claiming unemployment benefit when I was 19, was a different story to extracting money from the dole office today. Nowadays, you actually have to look for work. Back then, as long as you had a head, one arm and an address, all you had to do was sign a piece of paper and every two weeks skip down to the dole office to collect your free money. It was all too easy. After waiting in a queue for ten minutes, all I had to say was "I haven't managed to find employment in the photography industry yet, I'm afraid", and sign on the dotted line.

After collecting my first few giro cheques, I remember feeling incredibly guilty that hard-working taxpayers were funding my rent and buying me a few pints down the pub. The shame of sponging off the government weighed heavy on my mind, but it occurred to me one afternoon that I was not alone in my quest for an easy life. Standing in the dole queue, I noticed that the guy in front of me was using an expensive looking mobile phone. I didn't really think much of it, until I saw him wheel spin out of the car park in a top of the range BMW. After a while, I noticed more expensive mobile phones popping up and more people wheel spinning out of the car park in brand new vehicles. It became clear that there were many people taking the piss far worse than I was, and as the queue disappeared in front of me each fortnight, so did my guilty conscience. OK. So the money wasn't great, and I mostly had to live off baked beans and cheap biscuits if I wanted to have a social life. But when you're young you don't care, and besides, Si and my other student flatmates lived pretty similar lives to mine - getting stoned, eating crap food and watching TV all day.

It was after six months of living like this that I realised something had to change. On one overcast afternoon, whilst sharing a bench and a soggy bag of chips with a flea-bitten tramp on Streatham Common, it suddenly occurred to me that I had become a jobless bum. I was a free loader. An unemployed scavenger feasting off society. What was I doing here? And why was I having a conversation with a tramp about his pubic lice? My great plans had taken a major detour through Loser-ville and I needed to put them back on track. So that's exactly what I did. Waving goodbye to my smelly friend, I threw my UB40 in the bin, dusted down my camera and enrolled on a course in fashion photography.

The Pleasure Dungeon

There's a lively atmosphere in the drinking hole across the street from the steakhouse, and combined with the fact that Chris and I are now both extremely drunk, it's the perfect venue.

'This place is wall-to-wall with honeys!' Chris yells, perching himself on the edge of a barstool.

'Tell me about it. Don't look, but have you seen the redhead behind the bar?'

'Where?' Chris leers, turning around.

'I said don't look, you twat! She'll think we're desperate.'

'But we are desperate, aren't we?'

'That's not the point! Look, I bet you one dollar she'll be mine by the end of the night.'

'One dollar? You flash git.'

'Very funny. Watch and learn, mate. Watch and learn.'

Dressed in flared hipster jeans and a tight black vest top, the redhead smiles in my direction and takes a puff on a neatly hand-rolled cigarette. She then walks over in our direction, leans across the bar and replaces our ashtray.

'Take your time soldier,' Chris whispers. 'I know it's

been a while, but you don't want to fuck it up by rushing in.'

'What you talking about? This is my area of expertise, remember.'

'Yeah, right!'

'It's true! When you've got that special touch … you never lose it.'

'What special touch?'

'The one I used to pull Emily - the magic I use on all the pretty girls.'

'Si, you met Emily years ago.'

'I've had romances since!'

'Pissed-up one-night stands on the rebound more like. Name one girl you've pulled in the past couple of months that's been anything more than an alcohol-induced grope.'

'All right. What about that Charlotte girl I met in the K Bar.'

'What, that pretentious Chelsea it-girl?'

'Yeah. She thought I was the money!' I grin.

'She was fucked in the head.'

'*So*?'

'She was all over everybody that night. You could hear her biological clock ticking from miles away. You certainly didn't need any magic to pull that one.'

'OK, then. What about that nurse?'

'What nurse?'

'You know. The cute little nurse I met at Fabric with the pierced belly button.'

'What, the girl from Croydon who was only one court order away from being sectioned in her own psychiatric hospital?'

I shrug. 'And?'

'The *only* reason she went back to your flat, was to save herself precious stalking time by getting you to show her where you lived, rather than the freak having to find out.'

'Piss off! Anyway, you can talk. Since you and Chloe split up, all you've done is get drunk with the Queen's Park lads and have sex with your ex once in a blue moon.'

'What's wrong with that?' Chris smirks, scooping up a handful of peanuts off the bar. 'You'd do the same with Emily if you had half a chance.'

'Fuck off! She's damaged goods, mate. You'd never catch me going back there.'

'What, even if she rocked up one afternoon with a huge dildo in one hand and a pack of jonnies in the other?'

I shake my head. 'Uh ... no. No, I wouldn't.'

'Bollocks!'

'I wouldn't! Once its over - it's over for good. Now, hold onto your seat, Crissy-boy. You're about to see me perform magic way beyond the comprehension of David Copperfield.'

'Sounds serious. I think we may be in need of a shot.'

'Good idea.'

Turning towards the bar, I catch the girl's attention.

'Two shots of tequila, please,' I smile, fixing my stare for a second before glancing away. 'Oh ... and one for yourself.'

'Thanks,' she smiles flirtatiously, tucking her flame-coloured hair behind her ears.

Reaching up for a bottle of tequila, I admire her toned body and notice a colourful tattoo on the small of her back.

Spinning around, she places three glasses on the bar.

'There you go,' she blushes, avoiding eye contact. 'I hope you don't mind, but I've made them doubles.'

Straightening my posture, I look down at the shots. 'I guess there's no law against that.'

Sensing something is slightly wrong, I refrain from holding eye contact for too long, but then sneak a peek and see how her right eye appears to be looking in a slightly different direction to the other one.

'To Missoula!' I cry, raising my drink.

Acknowledging each other in turn, we knock back the shots - Chris retches at the floor, my eyes begin to water as I fight to take my medicine and the girl behind the bar slams down her glass, seeming completely unaffected by the potency of the drink.

'To tequila!' she giggles, reaching across the bar to light my cigarette.

'Yeah,' I croak. 'To tequila!'

*   *   *

With a fist full of change, Si goes in search of a cigarette machine, while I occupy myself by examining the paintings of cowgirls hanging on the walls. From the poor quality of the artists work, I presume they have been painted by some hopeful amateur, as the girls seem to ride on brown blobs and lie across yellow squares.

At the bar, I get chatting to a local cowboy from Missoula called Ben. He's a tough looking fella with a distinctive scar embedded in his face, and despite his *you-mess-with-me-and-I'll-mess-with-you* attitude, he seems to be a fairly nice bloke. He tells me about his childhood on a ranch, life in Montana and his bizarre collection of bullwhips, and before I know it he's got me in a headlock and has invited us both to a party back at his house.

Leaning against the bar, I rub my neck and introduce myself to a scruffy looking guy with blonde dreadlocks.

'Meet my buddy Kyle, but everybody calls him Flute.'

'How's it going, man?' he asks in a mellow tone.

'Fine, thanks. So why do they call you Flute?'

'Because I carry a flute around with me – look!' he

grins, removing a long shiny instrument from his jacket pocket.

'Cool! Can you play it?'

'Can he play it?' Ben smirks. 'Flute just happens to be a fucking master with the thing. Ain't that right, Flute?'

'Yeah, man. I'm pretty good!'

Darting a quick glance around the bar, he composes himself, then raises the mouthpiece to his lips and begins to play, swinging his head dramatically from side to side as if two thousand volts have just shot up his arse. I look on enviously as his wide eyes glaze over, and his dirty fingers dance energetically over the holes.

'What do you think?' he pants, flicking his dreadlocks away from his face.

'Not bad,' I reply, totally amazed.

'Fucking far out!' Ben yells.

'I've cruised the world with my flute and I'm the fucking Pied Piper, man.'

'The Pied Piper?'

'Uh-huh. You see, the world has taught me many things, and it has given me the faith to play this flute as though it were part of my soul.'

'Excellent! So where have you been travelling?'

'Oh ... you know. Here and there.'

'He's a cultured guy,' Ben nods.

'Such as?'

'I've been to so many countries, I don't know where to begin. Uh ... I went to Japan.'

'Japan! When?'

'I've just come back.'

'What was it like?'

'It was cosmic, man. Although, I didn't get to see too much.'

'Why not?'

'Was too stoned,' he chuckles, turning to Ben.

'Rock 'n' Roll, Flute!' Ben gives him a high five and

looks over at me to check my reaction.

'Did you fly into Tokyo?' I ask.

'Can't remember, dude. I hitched to Beijing, and then got a lift in this truck all the way to Tokyo. Man, it was a *long* fucking journey ... over mountains ... across hot deserts. You know, all that shit.'

'Isn't Japan an island?'

'An island? Oh ... maybe there was a bridge? No. It must have been somewhere else - maybe Africa. That's not an island, is it? What's with all the questions? Who cares anyway, right?'

Fearing that if all of Ben's friends are this full of shit, he might not be as sorted as I first thought. I mention his invitation to Si, who is pulling out all of the stops now to chat up the redhead behind the bar.

'Chris, chill-out! You're paranoid. He seems like a nice bloke. A bit strange maybe, but no different to anybody else I've met tonight.'

'I'm just making sure. He could be a fucking freak for all we know. The last thing we need is some whacko luring us down to his cellar, which he probably calls 'The Pleasure Dungeon', and satisfying his deranged fetishes by thrashing our asses with his bullwhips and spoiling our evening in Missoula.'

'Nah. It'll be fine.'

'You're probably right. He just seems a bit aggressive.'

'Stop being such a pussy - let's get laid!'

Realising that for once in his life Si is actually talking sense, I order another drink from the bar, and just as I'm about to knock it back someone knocks my right arm, causing the glass in my hand to slip through my fingers and smash on the floor.

'Oh, for fuck's sake!' I mutter under my breath.

'I'm *so* sorry,' a sweet voice replies.

I look up slowly and make the effort to try and focus on the blurry shape in front of me. It's a girl.

'I'll get you another ... what was it?'

'No. Please. Don't worry about it. These things happen,' I smile, looking deep into her liquid blue eyes.

Despite my beer goggles, I can see that she's absolutely gorgeous with silky blonde hair and beautiful breasts that make me want to scream.

'You sure?'

'Yeah. No problem.'

'My name's Jess, by the way. You're from England, right?'

'Yeah ... how did you know?'

'Ben told me.'

'Is he a friend of yours?'

'I wouldn't call him a friend exactly ... he's my bro-ther.'

'No way!'

'Uh-huh. We're very different. He's into bullwhips, and I'm into photography and art.'

'Great! So am I ... I mean ... I like art, and I take a lot of photographs. Who's your favourite artist?'

'My Uncle Jack.'

'Your Uncle?'

She nods. 'Yep. He's only been painting for six months. Since the accident.'

'Oh ... I'm sorry.'

'It's OK. It was the best thing that ever happened to him.'

'How come?'

'He was working for a timber company out of town, but in March he had a *real* bad accident. A log fell off a truck and rolled right over him. He broke his arm, leg, jaw, three ribs and fractured his skull. He was out of it for weeks - a lot of pain and stuff - and that's when he discovered God and art. I've never seen him so happy, I mean the God part scares me a bit - especially when he's going wild in church, but his paintings are amazing!'

'I'd love to see some of his work.'

'You can.'

'When?'

'Right now! Look around you, all of the paintings in this bar are his. Isn't that *great*?'

I look over at one of the paintings. 'Absolutely! They're ... uh ... beautiful. Your Uncle is *very* talented.'

'I'm so glad you like them. Most people think they're pretty lousy.'

I quickly change the subject.

'Hey ... Ben was telling me that bullwhips are a huge joy in his life?'

'A *joy*?' she snaps, turning towards him with a look of disgust. 'He'd marry one of those darn things if he could - he's obsessed! Anyway, forget about him, what are you guys doing now, because we're gonna head off soon and get the party started.'

'Lead the way!' I cry, jumping off my barstool. 'The night is but young!'

Spirit in the Eye

Flute staggers across the lawn towards the roaring fire in the middle of Ben's backyard. 'Man, this party rocks!'

'What a joker,' Chris sneers, as we hang behind, tentatively making our way towards the crowd of people silhouetted in the orange glow.

Loud music blasts from two large speakers balancing in an upstairs window, and as we reach the point of no return, we hear a voice calling to us from somewhere in the darkness below.

'Hi, guys. Welcome to the party.'

The light from the fire illuminates a grinning, frizzy-haired girl sat crossed-legged on a blanket next to a guy who's presumably her boyfriend.

'How's it going?' Chris replies.

'So cool! Harvey's done a great job of the fire. I'm Misty and this is Brent. Sit down and have a beer.'

We introduce ourselves and join them on the rug.

'Who do you know?' she smiles sweetly, fidgeting with a purple butterfly ring on her finger.

'Oh, we met a guy called Ben in a bar earlier tonight,' Chris replies.

'Aah … the birthday boy.'

'Is it his birthday?'

'Yeah. He turned thirty today, but whatever you do don't tell him I told you - it's a *very* touchy subject. He's seriously in denial. You guys been in Missoula long?'

'We only arrived here today,' I reply. 'We bought a van in Seattle and have been travelling around.'

She directs her loved-up eyes towards Brent. 'Cool! I've *always* wanted to do that.'

'You should. It's been amazing.'

'We can't at the moment. Brent has commitments with the church, so it's kinda hard to drop everything right now. Someday for sure. Do you two go to church at all?'

'No, but I had sex in a graveyard once,' Chris winks.

Cringing, I turn to Misty and flash my best 'he's only joking' smile.

Wriggling forward, Brent rests his arms on his knees and decides to jump into the conversation.

'Are you guys on your college semester?'

'No. I left college a while back and Chris graduated a few months ago.'

'So you're taking a sabbatical, then?'

'Not as such. We just thought we'd go travelling.'

Straining to hear what I'm saying over the loud music, Brent furrows his brow and nods his head furiously. He's an odd looking chap, with wispy fair hair thinning to the point of teenage baldness, and wearing an outfit obviously modelled on reruns of Starsky & Hutch. He pauses in thought for a good thirty seconds before offering a reply.

'Sounds like a lot of fun.'

'Hey...' Chris cries. 'I thought I recognised your voice from somewhere. You sound just like that character from *The Chipmunks*.'

Silence screams out around our small circle.

'The *Chipmunks*?'

'Yeah, you know! That cartoon with the three singing

chipmunk brothers. Your accent sounds like the guys voice - don't you think, Si?'

'You can't say that!' I whisper, shaking my head vehemently. 'He sounds nothing like Alvin, or Simon and Theodore for that matter!'

'*NO*! Not the actual Chipmunks themselves – that Dave bloke!'

I snigger, relieved that Chris has avoided yet another blunder.

'Dave?' Brent snaps. 'Who's Dave?'

'Dave's the human guy in it - their dad!'

'Their dad?' Brent frowns.

'Yeah. The Chipmunk's dad is called Dave?'

'The Chipmunk's dad is called Dave?' Misty repeats.

'Yes! *Dave*!' Chris grins. 'Jesus Christ!'

Misty throws Chris an evil stare. 'Come on, Brent. We'd better go and check on the pie. We brought a pie.'

She promptly grabs Brent's hand and drags him away from the glow of the fire. The flames lick around the edges of an old cardboard box, and I watch as 'Manigault Foods Here since 1905' is slowly eaten away so all that's left is a solemn 'Man'. We sit in silence for a moment.

'Nice one, Chris.'

* * *

Irritated by the religious freaks, I spy Jess sat on her own at the bottom of the garden. I abandon Si and go and chat to her.

'You having a fun night, Chris?' she asks, sucking on a slice of lemon.

'Absolutely,' I reply, battling to resist glancing down at her swelling breasts nestled beneath her tight white

T-shirt. 'It's not every day I'm invited to a house party in Missoula.'

'Yeah. I guess. So what's your first impression of Montana?'

'It's beautiful. I'm definitely coming back.'

'I hope so. I've got *such* a funny feeling about tonight,' she smiles, scrunching up her hair into a ponytail.

'Have you?'

'Yeah. A funny-happy feeling.'

'Sounds exciting.'

'Have you got a girlfriend back home, Chris?'

'A girlfriend? Oh … uh … no. No I haven't,' I reply, surprised by the question.

'Why not?'

'Well, I've recently come out of a relationship.'

'Oh … I see. You want to play at being single for a while?'

'Yeah, I suppose so.'

'Me too.'

'Really?'

'Uh-huh. I broke up with someone quite recently. A complete and utter asshole. We lasted for over a year, but he spent more time playing on his dumb computer than with me.'

'You're joking?'

She shakes her head. 'Nope. He's addicted to playing video games. We hardly ever had sex.'

'What a fool!'

'Like I say, he's an asshole. He's here tonight somewhere, probably on Ben's new X-Box. Anyway, enough about him. Why did you split up with your girlfriend?'

'Hard to say, really. I guess we just weren't right for each other.'

Committing your life to a relationship is a full-time job, and as any third rate daytime TV no-hoper will tell you, it takes hundreds, possibly thousands of hours of compromise and communication. Which is where it went wrong for me. Quite simply, the boredom set in, the communication dried up and the flame – well, the flame fizzled out.

It was on the morning of Chloe's 25th birthday when I realised our relationship was over. I woke suddenly in a blind panic, realising that I'd forgotten to buy her a present. I lay next to her in bed, racking my brains - trying to work out what the hell I could grab from my flat and wrap up. After agonising for a few minutes, I decided to go with plan B, and slipped quietly from under the duvet, threw on some clothes and ran to a local 'Everything's a pound' gift shop on the Kilburn High Road.

Skidding around the shop floor, I scanned the shelves for something cute and fluffy. Unable to think straight, I confessed all to the shop assistant, pleading her for advice. Pointing me in the direction of Toys 'n' Things, I grabbed the first thing I saw (which was, ironically, over a pound!) along with a tacky card with a big red silky padded heart on the front. Grabbing a pen from the counter, I scribbled a message inside and raced back to the house.

Tiptoeing back into the bedroom with the scruffy looking pink elephant and it's rattling eyes, I found Chloe sat bolt upright in bed with her arms tightly folded. She looked more pissed off than I had *ever* seen her before. A few weeks prior, she had discovered a stack of travel brochures under my bed and she knew instinctively that I wasn't planning a surprise holiday for us both. So arguing one last time, she packed her things and moved out.

Despite this being a distressing time for both of us, it didn't take me long to get over my guilt. In those early days you live a complete fantasy, the dream of sharing your life with that perfect partner - 'the one', who is everything you had hoped for. But things change, people change and it's not always for the good.

'Chris, have you ever swam naked?'

'Naked?'

'Yes.'

'Uh ... yeah.'

'Tell me about it,' Jess whispers.

'Blimey. Let me think ... it was at my local swimming pool.'

'You swam naked in a public swimming pool? Was there anybody else around?'

'Yeah. The place was packed!'

'*Really*? Weren't you embarrassed - or arrested?'

'No. It seemed a very normal thing to do.'

She squints at me. 'When was this?'

'Just over twenty-five years ago - I was eleven months old at the time. It was one of those swimming for mothers and babies classes. I've seen the pictures.'

'You're *completely* crazy you know that?' she smiles, reaching over and tapping me gently on the arm. 'But I like it.'

She stares hard into my eyes.

Clearing my throat, I whip a cigarette out of the packet and place it between my lips. 'So, what about you?'

'What about me?'

'Have you ever swam naked?'

'For sure! Lots of times. I love being naked,' she giggles. 'There's nothing more natural and free. Only yesterday I swam naked in my neighbours pool.'

'Bloody hell! Didn't they mind?'

'They're on holiday, stupid.'

'I was gonna say! Do you ever do it ... at night?'

'Do what at night?'

'You know. Swim ... naked?'

Jess purses her lips and leans forward. 'Are you trying to put ideas in my head?'

'Maybe.'

She reaches over and softly brushes her lips up against mine.

'Good.'

* * *

'Brent, I don't mean to offend you, but it really puzzles me how a person can believe so passionately and hold so much faith in the idea of God, when there's no way of ever proving he exists. It defies logic!'

'Simon, I don't ever force my beliefs on a person. People find the Lord in their own way. The only thing I can tell you, is that you may not be able to see or touch him, but he sees and touches you - in *every* way. I feel him with me every day, Simon.'

'Maybe I just haven't had the same experience as you. You can understand why I find it hard to believe in something that doesn't exist in physical terms, can't you?'

'Of course, but how do you explain what we are?'

'As you well know Brent, that's a question I'm unable to answer. But just because I can't explain the mysteries of the universe, doesn't lead me to believe the answer must lie in the existence of a higher force.'

'All you have to do is believe … and then you can see.'

'I don't feel I *need* religion to help me see. By coming to terms with the fact that I will probably never understand our existence, I'm able to appreciate the world for what it is.'

'I just think it's a shame you feel you have it all worked out Simon, because I can assure you, you're missing out on a whole lot of love,' Brent nods, placing a friendly hand on my shoulder.

'I do try and keep an open mind. All I'm saying is that I'm beginning to realise that you can waste a lot of life running around looking for answers, knock yourself out searching for happiness and contentment, only to realise that it *already* surrounds you in the beauty of the here and now.

Brent sits back and sighs. 'OK, but I'm still going to pray for you tonight,' he smiles, with a rather wry, maybe even camp smile on his face.

'Thanks, Brent. Maybe one day I will meet the great bearded one. For now, though, I think I'll just accept the inevitable - enjoy the ride and crack open another beer.'

'Sounds pretty deep, guys,' Misty interrupts. 'Simon have you met Tiffany?'

Looking up, I'm pleasantly surprised to see the redhead from the bar smiling down at me.

'Hi, Simon. How you doing?'

'Hey … Tiffany! I didn't think you could make it,' I reply, jumping to my feet.

'Why? Are you glad to see me?'

'Yeah!'

'Good, because I've got a little present for you.'

'Have you now?'

'A big bag of grass,' she whispers in my ear, '… and I could really use some help smoking it.'

'I'm sure I can be of some assistance.'

These days it's a rare event to meet someone I spontaneously click with, but Tiffany prompts an instant spark that ignites into a roar of flames, and immediately we become partners in crime.

'I just *love* getting fucked up,' she laughs excitedly, lying back on a giant banana shaped beanbag. 'There's no reason - I just *love* it!'

'I know exactly what you mean,' I mumble, tugging hard on a spliff end.

As Tiffany reaches for the ashtray, her vest top rides up to expose the tattoo on her back.

'Hey ... I noticed your tattoo in the bar. Very nice.'

'You like it?'

'It's beautiful.'

'I got it done a few years ago. Around the same time I lost my eye.'

She turns and looks at me confidently. I study her soft features and try to stare confidently back into her eyes. I now see that the pupil of her right eye is motionless, and it feels as though she's hiding something. I can't see in - the view is hidden from me.

'Did you notice?'

'No. Not until you just said.'

Drawing her close I kiss her full on the lips. 'I like it.'

'No you don't!' she laughs, pushing me away.

'I do! It gives you character.'

'I guess it's given me a kick up the ass. If I want something now, I just take it.'

'Well ... it shows in your personality. How did it happen?'

'It's *so* fucking stupid.'

'You don't have to tell me if you don't want to.'

She grabs the joint and pushes me back into the cushions. 'Well, the first thing to know is that I was stoned, so, you'd better watch out for me! And it was on my twenty-first birthday. I was trying to open a bottle of champagne...'

'It didn't blow in your face?'

'Not exactly. I managed to fire the champagne cork safely enough, everyone went crazy and stuff. But as I was rushing to pour it into the glasses, I slipped and fell on a bronze souvenir of the Statue of Liberty.'

'Ouch!'

'Tell me about it.'

Tiffany jumps up onto her knees excitedly and grabs my arm.

'Hey ... enough about my eye. Let's do some mushrooms,' she giggles.

'Have you got some?'

'Yeah. My boss got them for me.'

'You've got them on you right now?'

'Yep. You want some?'

She grabs her flimsy bag.

'No ... uh, thanks. I'd better not. Taking hallucinogenic stuff like that can be dangerous shit, you know.'

'*What?* Come on - it'll be fine! They're mild. '

'Nah ... I think I'll give it a miss.'

Tiffany stops fumbling inside her bag, and looks at me with disappointment in her eye. I'm unable to play along and eventually crack a smile.

'Only kidding cowgirl – *lets get high*!'

Getting Off

Apart from a cheap divers watch I bought from a petrol station on the Edgware Road, I'm stood completely naked at the side of a swimming pool.

'Is everything OK?' Jess giggles.

'Are you sure about this?' I shiver, dipping my big toe into the water. 'Your neighbours are definitely on holiday, right?"

'Yer. Don't worry.'

She slips off her knickers and throws them on top of her jeans. 'Let's go for a swim!'

Admiring her body, I watch as she kneels down and tests the water with her fingers.

She wrinkles up her pretty button nose. 'It's cold! I'm not used to this - it's as hot as a bath during the day.'

'Not to worry. We could always just chill out on the grass over there.'

'Are you chickening out?'

'*NO*! Of course not. Why would I do that?'

'You can swim, can't you?'

'Yes ... I *can*! I was top of the class at school, thank you very much. I even had a gold badge sown onto my trunks.'

'Ah, that's *so* cute.'

'I can't wait to get in there with you and do a few lengths.'

'Come on, then! Let's do it! On the count of three, right? One ... two ... *three*!'

I close my eyes and let my body take over. My mind tells me to stay put and not jump in, but my legs disengage from my brain and throw themselves off the side. I disappear with a splash into the murky darkness. My body feels paralysed with cold as I swim desperately up to the surface and gasp for air.'

'I can't believe you did it!' I hear Jess cry.

Catapulting myself onto the side of the pool, my body feels like one big goose bump. I turn towards Jess and shoot her an evil stare.

She places a hand in front of her mouth, desperately trying to control her giggles. 'The water must be really cold by the looks of things.'

I follow her gaze down to my privates.

'Very amusing,' I stutter.

Bouncing over to me, she wraps her arms around my neck and glues herself to my wet body.

'Where's your sense of humour gone all of a sudden?' she whispers, fluttering her eyelashes.

Fighting a smile, I console myself by enjoying the warmth of her breasts. 'Yeah, where has it gone?'

'Chris, come on! It was fun, right?'

'Oh, yeah. It was fun. In fact, it was so much fun I think you need to try it for yourself.'

'Thanks, but no thanks. I think I'll stick to swimming in the daytime.'

I scoop her up in my arms and hold her over the edge of the pool.

'*NO, CHRIS*!' she squeals, hitting me playfully on the shoulder. 'Put me down. *Please*! I'm sorry.'

'Well, how are you going to make it up to me?'

'I only brought you here because I knew it would be quiet. Swimming wasn't what I had in mind'.

I gently place her back down.

'Why? I reply, drawing her close. 'What did you have in mind?'

'The best time you've ever had.'

'Really?'

'The best...'

* * *

Falling into a dark bathroom, I slam Tiffany up against the door and slide the bolt across behind her. Kissing viciously she hangs from my bottom lip. I hold her at arm's length for a second and she looks up at me with wide eyes.

'Simon,' she whispers, as she slides down the door and begins to work at my belt.

Leaning against the wall for balance, I rest my head on my arm as she tugs at my jeans, close my eyes and concentrate hard on not passing out.

Managing to gain control, I suddenly hear muffled voices outside the window and realise that two people are arguing in the garden below.

'IF HE TOUCHES MY SISTER, FLUTE! I'LL FUCKING KILL HIM!'

'Calm down, man. He seemed a nice enough guy. Misty said she saw them going off for a walk.'

I peer down at Tiffany.

'Are you Ben's sister?' I slur.

Without stopping, she stares up at me and shakes her head from side-to-side.

'Good.'

I close my eyes again, but then flick them open in

horror and turn back to the window.

'*OH, SHIT*! I yell, pulling sharply away.

'What?'

'*ITS FUCKING CHRIS!*'

'What about him?'

Yanking up my trousers, I race out onto the landing. Everywhere is eerily quiet and feeling confident that the coast is clear, I tiptoe over to the stairs and edge myself along the wall. I vaguely remember seeing Chris sneak off through the garden with some cute blonde, and I realise now that it must have been Ben's innocent little sister.

Hearing a loud cracking sound, I feel my heart thumping inside my chest. The front door is wide open and I can see the pale blue light of the street outside.

'Fucking idiot!' I mutter, as I reach the last step.

Crawling on my hands and knees over the coarse hair of the doormat, I decide to take my chances and scurry across the front garden to the safety of a low wall. Breathless, I hesitate for a second before sneaking a peak over the top, and blinking in utter disbelief I witness a psychotic Ben punching his fist into the side panel of our van. I quickly duck back down behind the wall again.

Knees bent diddyman style I race along a row of cars and crouch low behind the back wheels of the van, holding my breath as Ben now lets his frustration loose on the bonnet with his bullwhip.

'*LEAVE IT, MAN*!' I hear Flute yell.

All of the windows are steamed up. I gently tap the glass and a hand furiously wipes away the condensation to reveal the terrified eyes of my brother.

'Open the door!' I mouth, as the van rocks from side-to-side with each karate kick swung at the passenger window.

Chris pops the catch on the door, and I snatch at the handle and dive headfirst inside.

'*JESUS CHRIST*!' I shout, seeing Jess in the back with mascara tears streaming down her face.

'*FUCKING HELL, SI*!'

Forcing my fingers inside the tight pocket of my jeans, I wrestle for the key.

'We weren't doing anything!' Jess sobs in despair.

Clambering behind the wheel I strike the engine, as Ben leaps hard at the front windshield like a rabid dog, screaming obscenities. Chris pokes his head through into the front and Ben pauses for a second in disbelief. We're both in there. With his sister!

This time he really loses it, and I'm afraid the passenger window's going to shatter.

'*CHRIS, LET JESS OUT*!'

Releasing the handbrake I reverse like a mad man. I hear the side door fly open and checking that Jess is clear, I floor the van in a half-circle and wheel spin off down the street.

Turning left and then right, we zigzag at speed through the deserted suburban streets of Missoula.

'*WE NEED TO HIDE*!' Chris yells.

'*HIDE*?'

'*YES - FUCKING HIDE*!'

Spotting a railway bridge, I pull off the main road and rally along a dirt track towards the cover of some trees. Fearing that Ben will find us, we turn off the lights and shakily smoke a cigarette, hiding like cowards in the shadows until daybreak.

Getting Out

I begin to feel sick as we pull into the motel the following morning, not solely because of Si's terrible uncoordinated driving, but also in reaction to the events of last night.

Trudging upstairs to our hotel room, we bump into Chad the housekeeper, who is standing outside our door with one hand on his hip and the other propping up a trolley full of clean sheets.

'It's check out time, guys,' he snaps, tapping his watch. 'You've got approximately four minutes and twenty-two seconds to vacate the room.'

'Bollocks,' Si groans, falling onto the bed.

'Sorry, but rules are rules.'

'Can't you give us just a few more minutes?' I grovel.

'OK, but I've got six more rooms to clean before twelve.'

Chad wheels his squeaky trolley over to the next room. I fall onto the other bed and lie with my head in my hands. 'I can't believe we ended up sleeping in the damn van after blowing cash on one night of comfort.'

'Yeah, but it was worth it!' Si grins. 'What a crazy, fucked up night!'

'We could have got into some serious trouble back

there. Especially driving down that road pissed - what the fuck were we thinking?'

Si stretches out and yawns. 'Nightmare! And who was that weird dude who drove our van to the party?'

'Shit. I wondered how we got there.'

'Hey, Chris! By the way - you owe me a dollar.'

'What for?'

'For pulling Tiffany the bar maid.'

'Piss off! It doesn't count.'

'Why the fuck not?'

'She had a glass eye!'

'*SO*?'

'Well, anyone can pull a girl with a glass eye, can't they? If I'd known that before hand I wouldn't have made the bet in the first place.'

'Just because she had a glass eye, doesn't mean she wasn't attractive!'

'OK! OK! Bloody hell, Si. You really liked her, didn't you?'

'Yeah. She was a cool girl.'

'Are you in love?'

'Don't take the piss. Although, I have to admit, she's the first girl I've met in a long time that I could actually imagine going out with.'

'Seriously?'

'Uh-huh. She was *beautiful*! Much more chilled out than Emily. It's strange, after all that heartbreak, if I had to choose between Emily and Tiffany now, I think I'd choose Tiffany. Emily was fucking boring. All she thought about was becoming successful, where as Tiffany's just cool. She's into sculpture. She knows how to have a good time.'

'Sounds serious.'

'Nah … the last thing I need is another relationship. Although, it's a shame we had to run off so quickly. I didn't even get her number. Maybe we should stay another night - I'll be fucked if I'm going to rush.'

'Yeah ... good idea. We should pop back to Ben's house and say hi.'

'Very funny.'

'Exactly! There's no way I'm sticking around here. It's a small town, he might come looking for us.'

'He won't bother.'

'He *might*! Let's just get the hell out of here.'

'Stop panicking! He doesn't know where we're staying, and besides, we need to get that hole patched up first.'

'What hole?'

'Where the transmission fluid's leaking out.'

'Shit. I forgot about that. Can't we just keep topping it up?'

Si shrugs. 'I suppose so.'

After a power shower and a change of clothes, I finally get my act together and push Si out of the room. Chad stands impatiently outside wearing a pair of yellow marigolds.

'About time,' he tuts, barging past us in the doorway. 'If my boss hears about this, I'll be in shitsville.'

'Moody bastard,' Si mutters, as we trudge across the car park.

'Come off it, he's a busy man.'

'So. We paid good money for that room. It's a shame we never actually slept in it.'

'Oh ... shut up.'

'What?'

'You're so stingy.'

'*Me*? You're the tight arse round here,' Si fires back. 'I bet you never thought to leave him a tip, did you?'

'I did, actually. I left him a bit of loose change on the bedside table.'

'What? Mr Tight Arse left a tip. You're kidding me?'

'Hey ... I'm not a tight arse!'

Lighting a cigarette, Si passes one over to me.

'No thanks, I've quit.'

'Since when?'

'Today - right now.'

'Seriously?'

'Yep.'

'*Why*?'

'I'm trying to get fit.'

'Don't make me laugh.'

'What's wrong with wanting to be healthy?'

'Chris, the last time you tried doing some exercise you collapsed on the floor after ten star jumps.'

'I twisted my ankle.'

'Yeah, right! If I remember correctly your exact words were "Fuck this shit, let's go down the pub".'

'Get off my back. All I said was I've decided to quit smoking. It's no big deal.'

'All right - go for it! More cigarettes for *me*.'

Spying a car wash up ahead, I develop a sudden urge to clean the van. Forcing Si to pull off the road, he lets out a sigh and parks up alongside a self-service Auto-Vac.

'Perfect,' I smile, admiring the powerful looking hose. 'We'll have this van clean in no time.'

'It's only going to get dirty again,' Si whines, rubbing his tired eyes.

'I know that. But it's lost its shine, hasn't it?'

'What is this obsession of yours with everything being spick-and-span and in its place?'

'Fuck off!'

'No, because it's true. It's like when we were kids, whenever you bought a new pair of trainers or a tennis racket, you'd spend hours positioning them at cool angles at the bottom of your bed.'

'No I didn't!'

'Yes, you did! You *freak*!'

'Look, just let me clean it – then we can get back on our way.'

'Hang on! I know what you're up to. You're trying to wash away your guilt after the sordid events of last night, you pervert.'

'Piss off! I just want to clean the fucking van, Si. That's all.'

'That's right, punish yourself for your sins. Well, you can't wash away shame, sicko!'

'You're just jealous.'

'Of what?' Si sneers.

'Jess.'

'*Jess*? Why the fuck would I be jealous of her? I got a blower, didn't I?'

'Come off it, I saw the way you were looking at her last night.'

'Don't be fucking ridiculous. Why on earth would I be jealous that you somehow managed to have your wicked way with a teenager?'

'She was twenty-one!'

'She wasn't my type, anyway. Her tits were too big.'

'Bollocks! And what do you mean "somehow managed"? She thought I was the bees-bollocks, thank you very much. She couldn't take her little hands off me, and she kept saying how much of a gentleman I was.'

'That's a first.'

'Well, maybe - just maybe I've changed, and have begun to realise the importance of treating a lady with dignity and respect.'

'Oh ... please.'

'What? I took Chloe to that expensive Conran restaurant near Tower Bridge, didn't I?'

'Only because you'd collected 'two for one' tokens in the Evening Standard.'

'So? It's the thought that counts.'

'Yeah, but you must have been really embarrassed

when you realised you hadn't collected enough tokens and had to dash out to buy a bloody paper?'

'Look, hippie boy! Stop reminding me of my little fuck-ups and let me clean the van.'

'Whatever turns you on.'

Feeding dollars into the coin-operated machine I grab the hose, hit the start button and wait for something to happen. The correct amount of four dollars appears on the cracked display, so I re-read the instructions and try pushing all of the other buttons. Nothing happens, and after a while I resort to whacking the top of the metal box with the palm of my hand.

'*HEY*! *HOLD IT RIGHT THERE*!'

Surprised, I look round and see an extremely tall man wearing a baggy Jazz and Blues T-shirt walking briskly towards me.

'What you done? Have you broken it?'

Stepping aside, I feel like the naughty kid caught messing about with the fire extinguisher in the school canteen.

'It doesn't work.'

'God darn it!' he spits, starring hard into my eyes.

Feeling rather awkward I dart a quick glance over at Si, who appears to be fast asleep in the front seat.

'This is the last time I'm going to fix this darn thing.'

I watch as he takes a screwdriver out of his tool belt, tuts, and at great speed, levers open a trap door at the front of the machine and begins poking inside.

'There we go,' he sighs, jiggling a mass of tangled wires. 'Now, have you pressed the Mega-Power-Spray button at all?'

'The Mega-Power-Spray button?'

'That big red button there.'

'I don't think so. I pressed one of them, but I can't be sure if it was that one.'

'Well, you should never press the Mega-Power-Spray

button before selecting the With-or-Without-Soap button - do you understand?'

I nod. 'Yes. I think so.'

'I'm gonna replace this pile of crap someday,' he repeats, shaking his head.

No time like the present I think to myself as he continues to fiddle around, yanking out a couple of wires and moving them closer to his face for inspection.

'What about my four dollars?' I nervously ask.

'What four dollars?'

'The four dollars I put in the machine - to wash my van.'

'You're shitting me, right?'

'No.'

He peers at the machine and then looks back at me. I smile and nod at the machine. He grins at me falsely and peers once again at the machine before sighing, shaking his head from side-to-side, and storming off back in the direction of his office, presumably to get my money, although, I can't be sure.

'Who was that?' Si asks, looking tired and confused.

'I don't know. The manager, I think.'

'What happened?'

'The bastard thing doesn't work.'

'Pity,' he replies smugly.

Deciding to try my luck at hoovering instead, I reverse up beside a vacuum cleaning machine. As the last of my coins drop into the slot, it kicks into life with an almighty boom and I dive excitedly at the carpet, while Si sits back and covers his ears.

'Do you want to have go?' I shout, pointing at the hose.

'No.'

'Come on! Where's the fun in owning a vehicle if you can't enjoy giving it a good clean?'

Si raises a middle finger before throwing my jacket over his head.

Feeling a tap on my shoulder, I look round and see the guy has returned with my money.

'I wouldn't waste your time with that thing. It only lasts for...' the machine cuts out, '...two minutes.'

With a low grunt, he turns on his heels and heads back towards his office.

'Bollocks!' I yell, whipping my jacket off Si's head. 'What a waste! I'll just have to use this shit brush.'

'You *love* hoovering, don't you?' Si shouts over his shoulder.'

'You what?'

'You can't get enough of it, can you?'

'Si, what's your problem?'

'I haven't got a problem. Admit it. Ever since we bought this van, you've spent hours sweeping the carpet - every little crumb seems to frustrate you.'

'No it doesn't!'

'*Every* little crumble makes your blood boil.'

'*FUCK OFF*! Well, what about you ... you bickering old wife. Always buttering the rolls and cooking the meals. You're a bloody nagging wife you are!'

'Is that right? Well, you're a sad, pathetic, brow-beaten, downtrodden husband; always insisting you drive and cleaning your precious van: "Oh, no! There's a bit of dirt on the wheels. I must clean it immediately!" You prick!'

'It doesn't bother me that you find stirring a pot of meatballs more fun than cruising the highways. Besides, it scares the shit out of me when you get behind the wheel - you wife!'

'*HUSBAND*!'

'*WIFE*!'

Microscopic Bum-Fluff

Stocked up with five bottles of transmission fluid, Chris sits happily hunched over the steering wheel, while I chill in the passenger seat mixing non-alcoholic cocktails and acting the DJ. The van seems to be running well as we zigzag across the wide-open plains of the 'big sky' state of Montana, and making our way south on highway 95 we feel confident enough to push on into the night.

Exiting the highway near to the town of Dillion we park in the gateway to a huge field, and climbing onto the roof of the van, we crack open a couple of beers and stretch out beneath the vast night sky.

'Now, this is why I like to travel,' Chris sighs. 'It's not everyday you get to see a sky as beautiful as this. Just look at all those stars - it's mind blowing!'

'It's fucking mad!' I whisper. 'They look close enough to touch.'

We both raise our arms and reach into space.

'Hey, Si. You know the hiss of static when you turn on your TV?'

'Yeah.'

'That's traces of radiation that still lingers from the big

bang around fourteen billion years ago?'

'Really?'

'Apparently. Also, there are supposed to be something like a hundred billion galaxies in the universe, each with billions of stars.'

'Where did you learn that?'

'I read about it at the dentists.'

'Wow ... amazing, isn't it?'

'I know. It's brilliant! Free magazines.'

'No! I mean *space*. It's incredible.'

'Oh, yeah ... there's shit out there that would literally make your dick shrink and your balls drop off.'

I shake my head. 'You're probably right! Somewhere up there is another life form. There has to be! It would be arrogant of us to think we're the only planet with life in the entire universe.'

'Excellent! Little green men,' Chris laughs.

'But what are we, man? We're nothing - microscopic bum-fluff compared to the rest of the universe.'

'Well, if it wasn't for that Galileo bloke and the Hubble Telescope, we'd still be scratching our arses and wondering what the hell is up there.'

'Yeah. Think how much the Hubble has shown us?'

'It's the Ferrari of telescopes,' Chris grins. 'It's able to capture faint images of galaxies that are more than twelve billion light-years away.'

'Bloody hell! Twelve billion light-years away?'

'Yep. That's nearly back to the big bang itself.'

'Space, Crissy-boy - the final frontier.'

Chris turns to me and frowns. 'I didn't know you were a *Star Trek fan*?'

'Do I look like I'm a member of a geeky sci-fi club?'

He nods vigorously. '*Yes*!'

'No I don't! Have you seen what those freaks look like?'

'No - have you?'

'Afraid so. I had to produce a live internet web chat

with this American bloke once, who was a famous orga-
niser of sci-fi conventions around the world.'

'Blimey, what was he like?'

'Weird! He arrived at the office in full Captain Kirk costume.'

'No he didn't?'

'He did!'

'My God! Haven't people got more important things to
do with their time, like ... *get a life?*'

'In theory, but he's not alone out there, Chris. It was
one of the most successful live interviews we ever did.
There was literally thousands of them online.'

'Unbelievable.'

Returning my attention to the overwhelming night sky,
I lose myself for a while in the enormity of space and
time.

'How can you not want to experience this?' I grin. 'I
mean, I've never seen the Milky Way this clear before.'

'Well, it beats the shit out of watching the telly every
night, that's for sure.'

'It makes you wonder doesn't it? Why do people work
so hard when you can just chill under the stars like this
for free?'

'It's beyond me,' Chris replies, flicking his cigarette at
the sky in a shower of sparks. 'I guess everyone's just
doing their *own* thing, aren't they? Lingering on the planet in whatever way suits them best.'

* * *

Si can sleep through almost anything. Even when I shine
a torch directly in his face, he just mumbles something
and carries on snoring. I, however, am a light sleeper and
tend to wake up around five-thirty every morning, particularly when living in a van with no curtains and a bed

the size of a child's cot.

Sliding the van door open, I step out into the fresh morning air, zip up my jacket and peer out across the misty fields. Walking over to a fence, I shiver in the cold as I point my camera at an old wooden barn that has long been abandoned. Tremendous yellow rays of light fill the sky as the sun appears over the horizon, and as the colours change I open the shutter and capture a moment in time.

As long as I can remember I've felt an overwhelming desire to travel and explore the world. When I was a kid, I would stand with Si on the banks of the Wash near Boston docks in Lincolnshire, and watch huge cargo ships sail by on their way to Russia or Scandinavia. Waving with excitement at the sailors, I would try to imagine what it must be like to venture across the world – would wonder whether I will ever do the same. At school, I would spend hours in the library with an atlas exploring the world laid out in front of me. From Bangkok to Bogota, Beijing to Buenos Aires, I would trace epic journeys from one continent to another and feeling butterflies in my stomach, I would say to myself "I'm going to go there someday". As a single guy from an affluent country, I find it hard to imagine why I wouldn't just pack up my crap and head off into the unknown, especially when the possibilities seem endless and the world is awash with colour that I find almost impossible to ignore.

Turning back to the van, Si's crazy hair appears out of the rear window.

'*HEY, CHRIS! HAVE YOU SEEN THE PACKET CHEE-SE?*' he yells, smacking his head painfully against the sharp metal frame of the window.

Hooking the camera strap over my shoulder, I glance out across the fields and smile in the knowledge of what we have become.

Midday at the Oasis

Soon after sunrise, we cross the border into Idaho and drive practically the entire length of the state in the cool morning breeze. Chris chews noisily on a greasy bacon sandwich, as we follow signs to a public swimming pool in the quaint little town of Pocatello.

'It looks closed,' he mumbles, tomato ketchup dribbling down his chin and splattering on the front of his T-shirt.

'I'll go check it out.'

Stepping inside I'm struck by the strong smell of chlorine and the tropical temperature of the atrium, that's filled with a jungle of hanging baskets, potted plants and trees. Surprising a chubby lady sat behind a kiosk in the entrance hall, I ask her what time the pool opens and she stares at me suspiciously, pushing a pair of big red glasses up the bridge of her nose.

'One o'clock,' she snarls.

'Great. Will there be loads of kids in there?' I ask cheerfully, concerned it will be packed with screaming rascals.

'Yes. Why?'

'Oh … no reason?'

Turning on my heels, I leave the building feeling a little annoyed by her unfriendly manner and passing the fun pool, I decide that it looks a bit over the top for our requirements.

'We can't go in there, it's more for kids.'

'I know what you mean,' Chris replies, stroking the dirty looking stubble on his face. 'It doesn't feel right, does it?'

'Shit! Has it crossed your mind that we probably look *really* dodgy parked up outside here?'

'Do you think so?'

'Yeah. I feel a bit out of place, like we shouldn't be here.'

To our right, screaming boys and girls play merrily on the swings in a park. A kid in a pushchair eats a giant ice cream, and a wave of discomfort creeps over me as I watch three youngsters skip across the grass on a day trip to Billy Goats Zoo.

Deciding to leave, Chris accelerates towards a pedestrian crossing, breaks clumsily at the lights and then stalls right in front of a motorcycle cop parked up beneath a tree. Glancing up from his notebook, the mean looking law enforcer stares in our direction from behind reflective shades. Striking up the engine again, Chris pulls carefully away, and I cringe as I feel the cop's stare burning into the back of our necks as we make our way down the street.

'Fucking hell, Chris. What are we like! Were we honestly about to go for a swim in a children's fun pool?'

'Yes. I *actually* think we were!'

'I can't believe it. Imagine what we would have looked like walking out of the changing rooms? Two big hairy blokes surrounded by kiddies, space hoppers and inflatable clowns.'

'Oh, fuck it!' Chris smiles, as we lose our way in an

idyllic white-picket-fence neighbourhood. 'We're just two young guys travelling the world - there's nothing wrong with that.'

'Yeah, but knowing our luck something bad will happen this afternoon and we'll be arrested as the main suspects.'

'Holy shit - wrong place wrong time scenario, *The Fugitive* style.'

'You may laugh Chris, but it happens. The system fails sometimes. People must get banged up all the time for things they didn't do.'

'Do you reckon?'

I nod. 'Definitely. I mean, imagine how bad that would be?'

Looking uncomfortable, Chris darts a look in the rear view mirror. 'Well, yeah. You'd be fucked!'

* * *

Putting the swimming pool disaster to the back of our minds, Si directs me down a quiet road that appears to lead nowhere. I begin to get agitated, so I pull over into a lay-by.

'What you doing?' he shouts.

I crank on the handbrake and turn down the stereo. 'I refuse to do another Freeway.'

'It says on the map there's a hot spring about five miles down this road. Have some faith!'

'Maybe we should forget it.'

'Don't be silly! I'm top-notch with a road map now,' Si grins, tossing it into the back of the van. 'It's not a problem. I know exactly where we are.'

'Good, because I'm starting to smell like a pigs arse.'

'Don't you worry me lad, I'll have you neck deep in a

natural spring before you know it.'

'Hey, Si! Look at that dude over there.'

An old man, who appears to be surrounded by the entire contents of his house, sits slumped in a deck-chair at the side of the road.

'Oh, yeah! What the fuck's he doing?'

'I don't know. Maybe we should ask him for directions?'

'Don't be ridiculous!'

'Why not?'

'I told you. I know where we're going.'

'There's no harm in asking, is there? He probably lives around here.'

'Chris, don't you think it's a teeny-weenie bit strange, that an old man is sitting on his own in the middle of nowhere along with all his worldly goods?'

'I guess so, but he still might know where the hot springs are.'

'He's not waiting for a pissing bus, for God's sake. The poor bloke's obviously senile, or deranged, or homeless!'

'How did he get here, anyway?'

Si shrugs. 'No idea. It's not like there's a car parked anywhere nearby.'

'Maybe he's waiting for someone?'

'It's more likely the reverse. His family grew tired of him, took him on a picnic in a removal van and on their way home stopped in this lay-by, waited for him to fall asleep and then fucked off. He must have woken up and wondered where the hell he was.'

'Come off it! No one's that cruel.'

'I think you'd be surprised.'

We sit back in our seats and watch him for a while, as he taps the top of a scruffy looking suitcase with his walking stick and rocks steadily from side-to-side.

'I know what's happened,' I grin. 'He woke up this

morning and while trying to squeeze the life out of a five day old tea bag, he thought to himself - it's time to move on.'

'Chris, I don't think an old guy like that would just pack up his shit and decide to head off on an adventure.'

'Why not? Take a look at us, we're in exactly the same situation.'

Si shakes his head incredulously. 'No. We're not in the same situation. You're getting all of this packing-up-and-shipping-out business mixed up with living on the streets; we're not homeless - we're just travelling. We've got money in our back pockets and some sort of direction, whereas that bloke is definitely *not* travelling.'

'I know he's not travelling you twat, but he's living outside the system in the same way as we are.'

'Maybe. I still think it's very different. At the end of the day when we run out of money, we'll return home and earn some more. He can't do that.'

'What shall we do, then?'

'What do you mean?'

'Should we go over there and make sure he's OK?'

Just as I'm about to open the door, a patrol car zooms past and skids to a halt beside the old man and his belongings.

'Time to go!' Si cries.

'What about the old fella?'

'He'll be all right. Let's keep moving.'

Following Si's orders, I pull sharply away and see the old man waving his walking stick in the air at one of the patrolmen, as he tries to defend what little he has left of his life.

* * *

We whiz past a wooden sign with 'Lava Springs Natural Spa' burnt into it, and park up against a stone wall by the reception.

Roman style fountains ripple in the tranquil gardens leading up to a large house, and weaving between three rectangular pools of steaming green water we pause on the steps outside.

Chris pokes his head into the posh entrance hall. 'Looks expensive.'

'It does a bit. You probably have to pay fifty dollars to dip your toe in.'

'Yeah, and another fifty to dry it on one of their fluffy fucking towels.'

'Oh … fuck it, Chris. I'm desperate for a swim. Let's check it out.'

Walking across the marble floor, we head towards a pretty girl dressed in a starched white uniform stood behind a trendy, frosted glass reception desk.

'Hi, guys. How can I help you?' she beams.

'Is it possible to use the pools, please?' I ask in a hushed, reverent tone.

'Sure. Are you members?'

'No … uh … sorry, we're not,' Chris replies, furrowing his brow.

She tilts her head to one side and shoots us a sympathetic smile. 'That's no problem.'

Placing a price list in front of us, she explains that it's forty dollars each to use the VIP pool, which includes a massage and a complementary vitamin drink, but only ten dollars for access to the smaller, less glamorous pool, which includes a couple of sun beds and not much else. Oh, and the towels are an extra five dollars.

'I think we'll give the VIP pool a miss. We're pretty poor at the moment.'

Chris turns sharply towards me, looking annoyed. 'Speak for yourself!'

'So *you'll* be using the VIP pool, then?' she smiles.

'Uh … well, no,' he blushes. 'We'd better stick together. We're sharing the suntan lotion, you see.'

Grinning falsely, she slides two white towels across the counter.

'That'll be fifteen dollars each please, guys.'

'Great. Thanks for your help,' I reply, pulling a crumpled note out of my back pocket.

'Oh … and if you wouldn't mind using the outdoor shower before entering the pool, that would be great.'

Feeling like a couple of disease-ridden rodents, we thank her again and make our way back into the garden.

Barely wetting my hair beneath the cold dribble of the outside shower, I leap into the smallest of the steaming pools and feel a rush of heat power through me.

'Ahh…' I gasp, floating on my back beneath a deep blue sky. 'This is the life! I feel like a king!'

'Wouldn't it be great if you had one of these in your back garden?'

'Damn, right! You don't realise what a luxury hot water is until you haven't got any.'

Eager to start work on a spot of sunbathing in preparation for the beaches of California, I vault onto the poolside. Water trapped inside my baggy shorts, rains from my crotch as I begin drying off on a sun lounger, and smothering myself in oil I bask in the midday heat. Nodding off, I'm rudely awoken by the piercing squeal of a child and squinting in the bright sun, I see that Chris has stretched out on the sun lounger next to me. Sitting up, I dab my face on the corner of his nice dry towel, and a second high-pitched squeal from the noisy infant prompts me to glance behind with irritation.

Two young couples at the far end of the pool stare back at me, and I'm unnerved by the look in their eyes. I reposition myself with my back to them and begin to feel quite uncomfortable.

Listening carefully, I swear I can hear hushed voices and then one of the women tries to contain a snigger. Looking over at Chris and then back at my long thin body stretched out on the sun lounger, I wonder what they make of us. We look a bit like George Michael and Andrew Ridgeley in the *WHAM!* 'Club Tropicana' video, minus the trumpets, and dwelling on this thought for a brief moment, it occurs to me that they probably think we're gay. It all adds up. This is cattle country for God's sake. Where men work all week on the ranch, go to rodeos at the weekend, *take* a woman, *raise* a family. Guys our age are supposed to drink and fight, sleep with whores, not spend the afternoon at a natural spa working on their tans.

Biting my nails furiously, burning but too embarrassed to move, I question what we're doing with our lives. Shouldn't we be married by now? Maybe we've fucked up in some way? Failed! Perhaps it's not the monotony of the nine-to-five that's the problem, maybe it's us? Most people seem fine, they just get on with things, enjoy the challenge of work and relationships and families and friends.

Dabbing my face again on Chris's towel, I disturb him.

'Get off,' he groans in a childlike voice.

Cringing, I hear another snigger from behind as he releases a high pitched yawn.

'Shall we have a swim?' he blasts out, blatantly unaware of the people behind us and the gayness of such a question from one man to another.

'You do what you like, mate,' I holler.

'What's a matter with you?'

'Keep your voice down!'

'Why?'

'Think how we must sound!'

'Oh ... right,' he whispers, taking a good look at the young couples before returning to me with a confused

132

look. 'Sound like what?'

'Work it out, you dumb ass! We look fuck-all like bro-thers, and we're too *old* to be innocent buddies just hanging out together during the college holidays. They probably think we're … you know!'

Chris continues to stare blankly in my direction. 'You've completely lost me.'

'My God, it's like talking to a fucking monkey. Think about it. They probably think we're … nancy boys, for Christ's sake!'

'*Nancy boys*?'

'Yes!'

'Si, how paranoid are you?'

'Am I?'

'Yeah. You doofus!'

Hearing the families talk about heading home, I wait until the childrens screams are out of range, and reclai-ming the pool as our own, I dive straight in and graze my knee along the concrete bottom.

'*BOLLOCKS*!' I yell, standing up waist deep in the sha-llow end.

Leaping into the air, Chris hits the water with a gigan-tic splash, and charging across the pool he grabs me in a headlock.

'*GET OFF*!' I shout, pushing him away. 'Did you see how young those couples were? That's what normal people do.'

Chris smirks. 'Yeah, but we're not *normal*, are we?'

'NO!' I yell, studying my raw knee above the water. 'At least I thought I was until I came on this trip!'

'Normal? You are joking?'

'What?'

'You were a fucking nightmare, Si - a disillusioned fre-akoid.'

Si frowns. 'Was I?'

'Uh-huh. You were well and truly sucked in. And I

hate to break this to you, but you were in real danger of turning into a pretentious wanker.'

'Fuck off!'

'It's true! It's time to put all of that London bollocks behind you now. You my lad have made the first step in regaining control of your life.'

'Do you reckon?'

'Absolutely.'

'It doesn't change the fact that we're no longer innocent young guys. People see us differently now, and it will only get worse as we get older.'

Leaning against the side of the pool, Chris kicks his legs to stay afloat. 'Look, all I know is that I don't intend to lead a boring life. It's like anything - work, relationships, *London* - it's all great for a while, but once the novelty wears off things become mundane and it stops being fun anymore.'

'True. Although, that doesn't solve the problem of people thinking we're freaks.'

Chris laughs and slaps the surface of the water with the palm of his hand. 'But who gives a shit what people think? I mean, why the hell would we stay in one place and work in the same career all of our lives when there's a whole world to explore? Who's to say we can't dabble in lots of things - stay flexible and live an alternative life?'

'That's all well and good, but how do you intend on funding that? Money is quite an important issue here, don't you think?'

'Is it?'

'Yes! You have to earn money to live, which is why we work...'

'I know you have to work – everybody has to work - but there's no reason why you can't be more in control of it. Who's to say you can't work for a few months, save up some cash and then hit the road for a while?'

'It's a nice idea, although, you still have to fund the

most basic lifestyle and let's face it, your CV isn't exactly bursting with skills and work experience!'

'Just because I haven't worked for the same company for five years, doesn't mean I'm unemployable. I'm as fit as a fiddle and able to learn. I don't need a high paid job to fund my lifestyle.'

'But temp work for the rest of your life isn't very cool, is it?'

'Who gives a fuck if it's *cool* or not? Working in the same job for twenty years isn't exactly rock 'n' roll. Besides, it's not for the rest of my life. What do you think I'm going to be doing when I'm not working? The idea is to use work to fund what I really want to do. I'm hoping that eventually I'll be able to sell some of my photographs or start drawing again. The possibilities are endless.'

'Fair enough,' I reply, splashing my face with the steaming water.

'Tell me something, Si. While you were working, how much of your pay packet did you save each month?'

'Uh ... not a lot. Why?'

'And what exactly did you spend your money on?'

'I dunno. Clothes, CD's, drinking, a few short holidays a year – what you getting at?'

'So, basically, you worked your ass off for eleven months of the year, in a job you hated, just so you could fund a lifestyle, which enables you to have absolutely no time to do anything for yourself, except pay for loads of crap you could probably do without.'

'Fuck off, Chris. The idea of a full time job is to provide you with the security to buy a house, pay into a pension, build yourself some assets. It's what our whole bloody society is built upon - long-term it makes sense.'

'What, so when you're old you can finally do the things you wanted to do when you were younger, except – hold on a minute - you can't because you're too *fucking old*.'

'Uh…yeah.'

'If you ask me, it's a bit of a gamble waiting until you're sixty-five to start living your life.'

'But a tiny problem remains, Chris: you can only live the lifestyle you're talking about whilst being single. There's no way you could afford to go exploring for a few months, and at the same time feed and clothe a family, especially on a crappy temporary wage?'

'Well, why the hell do you think I'm so keen to do it now? Come on Si, what's the matter with you? This is exciting! For the first time in years, your life is an open book. What you do now is entirely up to you. There are no rules, what you experience and learn from now on knows no bounds.'

'I've always quite fancied having a go at writing some poetry.'

'Go for it Wordsworth! Let's be artists in Amsterdam for a while - poets in Peru!'

'How about writers in Reading?'

'Reading?'

'No … you're right. Maybe not. OK, writers in Rajasthan. Explorers in Timbuktu!'

Tickle and a Tug

Eight months ago, I would have laughed if someone told me I would eventually end up travelling with my twin brother. Our lives were so different. While I was still bumming around at college studying fashion photography and pissing my student loan up the wall, Si had a good job working for an internet company based in Fulham, he had his own flat in Shepherd's Bush and a serious girlfriend. During this time, the very idea of him giving everything up seemed out of the question, and it was with genuine surprise that I was to learn all was not as rosy in his life as it first appeared to be.

I didn't hear from Si for sometime after my decision to leave London. He usually called at least once during the week, although, more often than not from his mobile while pissed out of his face in some bar. Free one afternoon, I decided to visit his office on the off chance he'd be around, and as I reached the main entrance I spotted him trying furiously to light a cigarette in the street outside.

'Hippie boy!' I waved, rushing over and playfully punching him in the arm. 'How's it going?'

Without expression he looked up at me, his long hair

hanging in front of his tired eyes, and pausing to catch a flame he drew hard on his Marlboro Light.

'Let's get a drink,' he quietly suggested.

Over pints of premium lager in a nearby basement bar, I quickly learnt that Si was suffering from a disorder common in people who have remained dissatisfied in their profession for a long period of time - better known as stuck-in-a-rut-itus.

'Chris, I don't know what to do.'

'Why? What's the problem?'

'Everything!'

'Everything?' I replied.

'Yeah ... everything!'

'Sounds serious. How's work?'

He shook his head. 'It's fucking brain-numbingly boring.'

'But I thought you liked your job at Global Massive Online?'

'I do! It pays well, I don't have to wear a suit, I meet some pretty interesting people...'

'So, what's the problem, then?'

'I don't know what the problem *is that's* the fucking problem!'

We both sat in silence for a few moments and peered down into our pints.

'Try to look on the positive side,' I grinned, trying to bring a little hope back into his life.

'There isn't a positive side,' he replied, tearing a beer mat in two.

'Come on. Cheer up! What happened to the good old Si, we know and love?'

'What do you mean by that?'

'You've changed. You've changed a lot. Are you sure you're not an alien who's taken over my brothers mind?'

Reaching over the table I tapped him on the top of his head. 'Who's in there? Go on! Hop it you little green twat.'

'Chris, what the fuck are you talking about? Can't you be serious for a minute! My life just happens to have hit rock bottom here.'

'You've definitely changed, pal.'

'Will you stop saying that!'

'No, because you have.'

'OK, how have I changed?'

'Well for a start you've been acting weird for ages and I've hardly spoken to you since my graduation. Let's face it, over the past few months you haven't exactly been a barrel of laughs, have you? In fact, you've turned into a right bitter bastard.'

'Piss off! No I haven't.'

'Sorry - but it's true! Since you started working you've become a miserable sod.'

Si shifted uncomfortably in his seat. 'Have I really been that bad?'

'Bad is an understatement!'

'I guess I'm just tired of the same old routine. Since things ended between me and Emily there doesn't seem to be much point to it all.'

'You've split up with *Emily*?'

'Yeah, last week,' Si replied, dropping his gaze.

'My God! Why didn't you tell me?'

He shrugged. 'I don't know. Embarrassed, I suppose.'

'*Embarrassed*?'

'Yeah. Well, you and the other guys always said it would never last.'

I sipped my beer before flashing a smile. 'Don't be stupid! You were seeing each other for four years - you met when you were too young.'

'I guess.'

'So, what happened?'

'I don't really want to talk about it.'

'Why not?'

'It's too personal.'

'Shut up! It's your twin brother you're talking to here! Telling me about it might make you feel better.'

'But you're the most insensitive cunt I know.'

'Thanks.'

Si leaned forward and rested his elbows on the table.

'OK,' he whispered, 'but promise me you won't take the piss?'

I shook my head. 'Course not!'

'Well, it all happened last Sunday. We went to Hampstead Heath, as me and Emily often did at the weekend. We found some shade under a tree and after a while we were ... you know, mucking around and play fighting. She was tickling me and I was tickling her...'

'You cheesy bastard!' I laughed.

'Fuck off, Chris! You know how it is. It was a beautiful day.' He paused, savouring that last memory. 'We were both in high spirits.'

Leaning back in my chair, I folded my arms and contemplated the situation. 'Hmm ... I *just* don't understand. Everything sounds like it was hunky-dory to me. I've always thought play fighting was a sign that all was well between a loving couple - obviously not. Was there any baby-language between you during your time together on that particular Sunday?'

'Yeah, a little ... why?'

'How little?'

'Chris! What's with the Agony Aunt bullshit?'

'Hush my troubled one!' I whispered.

'Shut up! I wish I hadn't told you now.'

'Sorry. No, seriously. Were you both talking baby-language, or was it just her?'

Si sheepishly peered down into his pint. 'Uh...'

'Don't be shy, this is important.'

'*Yes* – OK, we were both talking baby-language. Are you happy now?'

I took another large gulp of beer. 'Well, fuck knows

what was going on there? Play fighting *and* baby-language. It all sounds like a perfectly healthy relationship to me. There must be something else?'

'I only wish I knew, Chris? The next day she just ended it. Game Over.'

'The next day? What, just like that, "your dumped"?'

He nodded. 'Pretty much. Well, in all fairness to her, she did mention in passing that maybe we should have a break first - you know, give each other some space. Then I called her a slut, and I think that kind of sealed our fate more-or-less straight away.'

'What a bitch!'

'I know. I just can't get my head around it, although, we'd been arguing a lot. Maybe the writing was on the wall? Oh ... I don't know. I need some help here.'

'She was pretty fit.'

'And that helps me ... *how*?'

'Sorry. I mean, it makes any rational thoughts about the relationship impossible. Even if you are unhappy you just think, will I ever pull anyone as fit as her again?'

'I just can't get my head around it. I guess it had to happen eventually. It's weird, though. In a strange way I feel sort of relieved its over.'

'Really?'

'Yeah. When I left her house that day it was as if a huge weight had been lifted off my shoulders.'

'Ah! Now I see!'

'See what?'

'The reason why you're a bit pissed off.'

'Obviously! I've just been dumped by my bird.'

'No ... no my good friend. You're not just pissed off because you've been dumped by your bird, you just don't know what the *fuck* to do next - you buddy-boy are disillusioned. Let's face it, you're bound to be feeling a little lost, you've just spent the past four years living your life with someone else in mind.'

'How do you mean?'

'Well, think about it? Would you still be stuck in that job of yours if you hadn't been seeing Emily?'

'Fuck, I don't know. I guess I've wanted to leave for ages.'

'Exactly! You've been so busy pleasing other people that you've forgotten what it's like to be flexible and free. You have wings young Raven - you should spread-um!'

'Do you think so?'

'Uh-huh. Have you thought about your future much lately?'

'My future?'

'Yeah. What do you really want to *do* with your life?'

Anxiously biting his fingernails, Si starred down at the torn up pieces of beer mat on the table. This wasn't an easy question to answer. It's the question of all questions. A question that baffles even the rich and famous, a question that cannot be answered quickly. It's a question that can either make you jump into action or die miserably in the gutter.

'I don't know!' Si mumbled, his right leg shaking vigorously beneath the table.

'Perfect.'

'Oh, thanks, mate.'

'No, seriously - that's perfect! You're in exactly the same situation as me.'

'What do you mean?'

'It's simple. The answer to all of your problems is starring you right in the face.'

'Is it?'

'*Yes*! Come to America with me!'

'Don't be stupid! I've got commitments. I can't just drop everything when I've got commitments.'

'What commitments?'

'There's my flat ... my career. London!'

142

'I thought you just said you hated your job?'

'I do.'

'Well, fuck your flat - fuck your career!'

'I can't just jack it all in. It's easy for you to say, you've never had a proper job.'

'Si, listen to me. It'll be amazing! Stop thinking of reasons why you can't go - *just do it*!'

Deep in thought he paused for a moment, and whilst stubbing his cigarette out in the ashtray he looked up suddenly with big blue and bloodshot eyes.

'Shit! Maybe you're right!'

'I know I'm right. Well, think about it. Why wouldn't you?'

'*Yeah*! Why the fuck wouldn't I?'

'That's the spirit, Si.'

Jumping to his feet, he grabbed his cigarettes off the table and wrestling to get an arm through his jacket sleeve, he quickly downed the last of his pint.

'Where you going, you tit?'

'Chris, I'm off to do something I should have done a long time ago.'

'Really? What's that then?'

'*RESIGN*!'

* * *

Si drives steadily all the way to Provo. It's midnight, and to the delightful vocals of Willie Nelson blasting from the speakers we skid into an empty shopping mall car park. Apart from a trolley crashed into a nearby telephone booth, the van's the only thing with four wheels for miles around, but we're far too tired to worry about being robbed at gunpoint and climbing into our sleeping bags we happily pass out.

Rising early we spy the golden arches of a McDonalds, and within seconds of waking Si is sipping a bitter tasting coffee and watching me devour a double dog and egg stuffin-McMuffin burger in record time. Slumped in silence, I try to make sense of the day and peer blearily at the Salt Lake City Tribune abandoned on the table in front of me.

Plastered across the front page is a photo of Tom Green, a local Mormon who is on trial for polygamy. He's been convicted and sentenced to five years in prison for marrying five women and fathering thirty children, and it's the biggest polygamy trial in the United States for fifty years.

'Lucky bastard!' I grin as Si strains to read the article upside down.

'Why lucky? He got five years.'

'Yeah, but *five* women. Imagine that! Do you think he had them all at the same time, or separately?'

'God knows. Hopefully he got his money's worth for five years in the slammer.'

'Be worth it, though,' I whisper, looking dreamily towards the ceiling fan.

'You couldn't handle five you fat fucker!'

'Yes, I could! It'd be easy.'

'Bloody hell, Chris. With a sexual appetite like yours, it's amazing you've ever held down a relationship for more than one night.'

'What do you mean?'

'Well, were you faithful to Chloe?'

'No.'

'*Really?*'

'Yes. I cheated on her.'

'Who with?'

'It was purely accidental. I didn't do it maliciously - it just happened.'

'OK. Now answer the question.'

'It was at Dan's engagement party. The night I went back to Linda's house...'

'You didn't fuck Linda?'

'*NO*! Bloody hell, Si. Linda's a mate.'

'Well, who was it, then?'

'It was her flat mate from Guadalajara.'

'Where?'

'It's a city in Mexico, I think.'

'A Latino girl – good lad! Did she speak English?'

'A little.'

'Was she nice?'

'Not exactly,' I reply, screwing up my face. 'In fact, she was really, really ugly.'

'What, *really* ugly?'

'Let's just say she looked like she'd done a few furlongs tied to the back of a race horse.'

'Jesus Chris! I thought Latino girls were supposed to be hot as fuck?'

'Not this one.'

'You idiot! Did you feel guilty afterwards?'

'Of course I did, but these things happen sometimes. Besides, we were going through a difficult patch in our relationship.'

'Still, that's no reason to cheat on her. Especially if the girl was a moose.'

'True, and I'd probably feel a lot worse about it if I hadn't found out a few weeks after she moved out that Chloe had been doing the dirty on me.'

'What a bitch! Sounds like it wasn't a very healthy relationship to begin with.'

'Yeah, but then what is a healthy relationship? I mean, look at the adverts in the back of this newspaper: "Blue Bells Massage" – "Angel Escorts" – "Looking for love?" Are you telling me that everyone using these services is single? Imagine all the men who can't resist a quick tickle and a tug on their way home from work. People cheat - it's a fact of life - and just because you settle down with a partner doesn't mean your natural urges are going to suddenly disappear. Especially if the sex in your relationship becomes, well … *routine.*'

'Chris, sex isn't necessarily the most important thing in a relationship you know.'

'Uh, what fucking planet are you from?'

'It's not! Being soul mates and growing old together is important too.'

'OK. But if sex becomes as routine as a commuter train, and a roll in the hay becomes a birthday treat, *how* do you combat your sexual frustrations without hurting your partner's feelings? You could never admit that you're bored or crave a bit of variation in the sack, that is unless you're into the swinging scene I suppose!'

Si shrugs before glancing down at the advert for Blue Bells Massage. 'Maybe as the years pass, you just turn a blind eye to what's really going on; security becomes more important. Although, there must be some couples out there who remain faithful to each other. Aren't there?'

'Do you reckon?'

'Sure. Some cool couples manage to talk openly about things, or are lucky enough to have maintained a healthy sexual relationship.'

'Maybe. Although, if you looked into it you'd probably find those couples are the swingers.'

* * *

We decide to check out Provo while its still early. The roads are empty at this time in the morning, and enjoying the drive through the clean streets of town, we admire the grand looking football stadium, and appreciate the authentic looking buildings along the old high street. Chris reads aloud from a tourist booklet, and I'm intrigued to discover that the Mormon's settled in Utah in 1847, when they claimed it as their home, and successfully irrigating the land found ingenious ways to survive in the desert.

Approaching a modern church high above the city, the sun shines brightly as we look out over the huge salt lake that sparkles in the distance. There's absolutely nothing beyond the city perimeter for miles around, and I take a moment to appreciate the Mormon's incredible achievements over the last hundred and fifty years. Considering it's still early on a Saturday morning, I'm surprised by the amount of young people up and about, jogging around and playing football. We're in the college district and as we head towards the golden spire of the church on the hilltop, it occurs to me that if we were in England ninety-five percent of students would still be in bed nursing fantastic hangovers from the night before.

Standing outside the impressive whitewashed structure, Chris feels inspired to take a few holiday snaps and balances his camera on top of a rubbish bin. He sets the timer and jumps into view.

'This place seems a bit too good to be true,' I remark, as a group of healthy young women jogs by totally unaware of our existence.

Chris nods enthusiastically. 'I know what you mean. It's almost a bit *too* perfect.'

'According to this book, seventy percent of the population of Utah are Mormon, which means no sex before marriage, no alcohol, no gambling, no coffee and no homosexuality on the menu.'

'Don't be ridiculous.'

'It's true! The Mormon religion is *really* strict.'

'You're trying to tell me, that those lads playing football over there have never drank a beer or done the business in their lives?'

'Yep.'

'Bollocks!' Chris smiles. 'It's not possible. I don't believe it for a second.'

Crossing a neatly mowed lawn, a sign forbids any person who is not a missionary from using the area, and avoiding the sprinkler as it works hard to keep the grass green, we're pushed forcefully back in the direction of the car park.

Deciding to move on, we drive towards the highway and I turn my attention to what lies ahead. Part of me desperately wants to believe that this place is as perfect and wholesome, as it seems, but as the signs for Las Vegas loom ahead, I find it hard to not be sceptical when the ultimate playground of pleasure parades itself seductively on their doorstep.

* * *

The Escalante Desert is reaching boiling point, and at 111°F you could easily cook a greasy spoon style fry-up on the bonnet. Sweating from every pore, Si points out our serious lack of air-con, yet winding down the window and sticking your face in the wind certainly makes you feel as though you're really on the road and not living in an A/C bubble.

We stay on Highway 15 for as long as we can bear, but seeing an unlikely sign for a lake up ahead, we take the gamble and take a ten-mile detour along a dusty road.

'Have we died and gone to heaven?' Si cries, as the incredible turquoise blue water of Lake Soda, leaps dramatically into view.

Sparkling in the sunshine, golden dunes surround a wide open plain of beach that leads down to the waters edge, and crowds of people spill out into the shallows. Reaching a small wooden hut at the entrance to this bizarre oasis, we pull up and peer inside at a young kid drenched in sweat.

'Are you here for the lake, sir?' he sighs, mopping his forehead with a hanky.

I frown. 'Uh ... yeah.'

Poor kid I think to myself, he looks so bored and sweaty. He should be a lifeguard on the lake, flirting with the girls and saving lives. Not be locked up in this tiny oven.

'Just the one vehicle, sir?'

'Yes,' I smile, taking a few dollars from out of the conveniently positioned tray beneath the stereo.

'Thank you, sir. Park wherever you like.'

Wheel spinning across the bright white sand, we spot a lonesome tree offering superb shade only a few hundred yards from the waters edge, and before we know it we're stripped to the waist and dancing around in bare feet.

'What a bonus!' I yell, tilting my face in the sun.

'Yeah. It's mad,' Si grins. 'One minute we're driving through the desert and the next thing you know we're at the beach.'

I walk a few paces from the tree and look back. 'Why hasn't anyone else nicked this shade?'

He shrugs. 'I don't know. Everyone seems to have parked up alongside the lake. They must be hardcore lakers *shade's for pussies*!'

Enjoying an afternoon of sunshine, a quick dip in the blue and a pleasant lunch of tinned potatoes and steak chunks in gravy, we prepare to head back on the road feeling re-energised and ready for Vegas.

149

Throwing the keys to Si, I go in search of the toilets and find a portacabin behind the dunes. Inside the heat is immense and concentrating hard on breathing through my mouth and not my nose, I position myself at the steel urinal.

Hearing the door swing open behind me, heavy foot steps clomp across the floor.

'Goddamn bladder,' a man mutters, unzipping his flies beside me.

Ignoring him, I turn to the words 'Cunt Face 96' scribbled in red ink on the wall.

'Ah … there we go,' he sighs, looking down at my bare feet as he sways his hips from side-to-side.

Flashing him a quick smile, I notice a tiny black beetle running maniacally along a pipe above my head. 'Ever driven a juggernaut, kid?' the burly bushy-bearded bloke wheezes.

'No,' I reply, as I try to concentrate on the job at hand.

'My truck's got a stand-up kitchen, a TV and internet too.'

I throw him another cheesy grin, and continue to watch as the beetle completes its epic journey along the pipe.

'Right, then!' the guy mumbles, zipping up his flies, and releasing a loud fart as he makes his way outside, I struggle to contain a snigger.

Washing my hands in the tiny sink, I study my face in the mirror. My eyes look tired and my nose and cheeks are red from the sun. Suddenly, an idea springs to mind that is utterly ridiculous in these conditions. The problem is, since leaving England I haven't had much privacy, and any opportunity to provide myself with a little light relief has been few and far between. Unable to shake the idea from my weak mind, I seize the moment and throw myself into a cubical, whip down my shorts and enthusiastically set to work, at solving my unfortunate problem. Predictably, it isn't long before the pain kicks in, and as beads of sweat run into my eyes and my legs turn to jelly, I wrestle to conjure up absolutely any kind of erotic images, from past sexual encounters to Britney Spears dancing wildly in hot pants. Unfortunately, the survival instinct kicks in and my attention turns from sexual frustration to saving my life. I pull up my shorts with lightening speed, slam open the cubical door, tap-dance across the piss-covered floor and fall pathetically onto the hot sand in a quivering heap.

The Strip

Determined not to skimp in the city of pleasure, Chris suggests we concentrate all of our money on women and booze, and ditching the van in the multi-storey car park of the glamorous Mirage Hotel, we prepare ourselves for one long night of debauchery.

With each step more surreal than the last, we walk hypnotically from one insane illusion to another until we find sanctuary in a stylish bar deep within a casino.

'Jesus Christ! This Vegas place is a head fuck,' Chris grins. 'It's like being trapped in a fever-induced nightmare. I feel all disorientated.'

Ordering a couple of whiskies from a bunny girl waitress, a spotlight suddenly reveals a small stage in the corner of the room, and three stunningly attractive black girls burst into an Aretha Franklin cover - accompanied by a live band. Under normal circumstances 12:30 in the afternoon would be a little early to indulge in spirits, but sipping the first of many drinks I readily accept Vegas, the city without clocks, is not 'normal circumstances'.

'Hey, Si! Let's get married, baby!'

He frowns. 'Nah. You're all right.'

'Not to me - you spazza.'

'I know! Ha-ha! Actually, talking of getting married in

Vegas, a guy I used to work with flew out here with his fiancé and they had one of those drive-through weddings with an Elvis priest.'

'Tackerama!' Chris beams, raising his glass. 'If you're gonna take the plunge you may as well have a laugh in the process, although, it would take a hell of a lot more than a trip to Vegas to persuade me to get hitched at this stage in my life.'

'What happens if you meet the right girl? You're walking down the street and ... *SHHBAANG*! You bump into the woman of your dreams right outside Burger King.'

'How romantic!'

'OK, then. You're just coming out of the toilet in some Vegas bar and ... *POW*! You fall helplessly in love with a big-breasted country and western singer called Mary Lou.'

'Now, that's more like it!'

'So you would get married, then?'

'No fucking way! I haven't even started travelling yet. How can I be flexible and free if I've got a ball and chain hanging around my neck?'

'But, aren't you worried you'll grow old and wake up someday *really* well travelled, but on your own?'

'Si, any relationship built out of insecurity like that would be destined to fail. Who's to say you have to be married and have kids by a certain age anyway? George Clooney doesn't seem to worry about it.'

'Yeah, but he's a multi-millionaire Hollywood movie star. He hardly has to worry about being left on the shelf.'

'Si, being left on the shelf is something women worry about, mainly because they're deafened by the ticking of their biological clocks. It's not the same for blokes, and it would be a *really* bad idea to tie yourself down to a wife and kids unless you're one hundred percent committed or settled in some way.

'I'm sure some men manage it.'

'Well, if you ask me, it makes a fuck of a lot more sense to wait until you're ready.'

'So, if I started dating a girl my age now, in four years time she'd be thirty and ready to have kids, right?'

Chris nods. 'Probably.'

'Well, I can't see myself being ready for kids when I'm thirty, so we'd break up and the relationship would have been an utter waste of time.'

'You could always go out with someone younger.'

'A *lot* younger! Say I get married when I'm in my fifties like Michael Douglas, and marry a girl in her thirties like Catherine Zeta-Jones, that would make her about ... hang on ... *ten years old* now!'

'Let's go to jail, boy!' Chris laughs.

'You sick fucker! But do you know what I mean? The future mother of your child could potentially, at this moment in time, be wearing her mum's shoes and dreaming of becoming a famous ballet dancer.'

'Si, that is a truly frightening and twisted thought. Get me another drink immediately!'

* * *

After watching Rod Stewart sing 'Maggie May', or rather an overweight middle-aged has-been called Blake Rogers sing 'Maggie May', we head for the nearest exit and flag down a passing taxi.

'Chris, please feel free to correct me, but I do believe we have reached that special time of the evening.'

'What, that special time where we blow all of our money in a sleazy strip joint?'

The taxi screeches to a halt and I double-take as the

driver's head pokes up over the window. He's about four feet tall.

'Get in,' he squeaks.

We're welcomed inside by the strong smell of stale body odour, mixed with unwashed pants and questionable bodily fluids. Gasping, I pull my seat belt across my chest with one hand and cover my nose with the other.

'Fucking hell! I dread to think what action this taxi's seen,' Si mumbles.

'Where you wanna go?' the little Mexican fella asks.

'A strip joint, please,' Si replies, turning to me with a huge smile.

'What you looking for?'

'What's on offer?' I fire back.

'Topless girls, big titty girls, small titty girls, girls with snakes, live sex shows, mud wrestling shows, you name it buddy - Vegas got it!'

'Topless girls, please!'

'No problemo.'

We're glued to the seat as he speeds off, weaving perilously between the traffic along the main Strip. Feeling something soft and slimy under my leg, I raise my arse to find a used condom stuck to the back of my trousers.

'*JESUS CHRIST*!' I scream, grabbing the end and flicking it out of the window.

'Classy!' Si laughs, his hair blowing furiously in the wind.

I attempt to ask the taxi driver how much further it is, but he seems far too preoccupied to answer, muttering obscene words to himself and tapping his tiny fingers to the Latino music blasting from the stereo.

Eventually we arrive at a place called Freddies. Slapping some money into the driver's little hand we make our way through a pair of open neon legs up to the entrance.

'Now this looks more like it,' Si whispers, as we approach the red velvet rope, desperately trying to exude
confidence infront of two ape-sized bouncers guarding
the door. Grunting good evening in their direction we
walk right through without any trouble, but feel a little
apprehensive as we make our way down a purple vagi-
nal corridor before pushing through double doors into
the magic kingdom. Everywhere we look there are beautiful half-naked girls running between tables, jumping
on laps, spinning around on roller skates, pouring shots
like it's water and sliding down poles in front of nervous
looking men.

'Holy M-Mother of Babylon,' Si stutters, as he stands
paralysed by the amazing sight in front of him.

We take our positions at the bar and order two large
Jack Daniel's in an attempt to slow down our heart rates.

'Keep your eye on my drink, Chris. I need a slash.'

'OK, but be careful you don't get ambushed by a couple of busty chicks on the way,' I shout, watching him
weave through a crowd of pot-bellied gentlemen.

Feeling vulnerable on my own, I try to relax by taking
a large gulp of whiskey and turn my attention to the
entertainment on the stage. Absorbed by a scantily clad
young woman with a talent for manipulating tassels, I
realise too late that the fast moving object in the corner
of my eye is heading straight for me, and I'm surprised
as a large pair of breasts crash into my face.

'Oh, my God! I'm *sorry*,' the beautiful girl on roller skates giggles in a soft Marilyn Monroe voice.

'No problem,' I smile, grabbing hold of her arm.

Using my shoulder for support she lowers herself onto
the stool beside me.

'Thanks, honey,' she smiles. 'I'm so clumsy. I've only
been working here a week and I'm still trying to master
all this skating around.'

'That's OK. In fact, it's my pleasure!'

'What's your name special?' she asks, sucking in her cheeks and quivering her strawberry red lips.

'Uh ... Chris.'

'You're sexy. I'm Lucy, but you can call me Juicy.'

'Thanks. Nice to meet you,' I reply, shaking her hand, which seems faintly ridiculous considering that I've already had her tits in my face and she's sat next to me half naked.

We sit in silence for a few seconds.

'Can I buy you a drink?' I ask.

'Sure. I'll have a large Alaskan-Black-Ball-Breaker with a slice of lemon.'

'Alaskan, *what*?'

The girl behind the bar begins to throw a variety of spirits into a cocktail jug, and after a hard shake she pours a florescent yellow liquid into a glass.

'Try some - it's the *bomb*!' Juicy giggles, sliding the glass in front of me.

Curious, I taste the foul looking mixture and I'm surprised by its strength, so I order two more. Swiftly downing her drink, Juicy leans forwards and moves her glossy red lips up close to my ear.

'So,' she whispers. 'Would you like a private dance?'

I glance down at her breasts. 'Uh ... yes ... absolutely!'

'Then follow me honey,' she pouts, leading me away by the hand.

Suddenly, Si returns to the bar grinning from ear to ear. '*UNBEL-FUCKING-IEVABLE*! These girls love it, Chris! They just fucking *LOVE IT*!'

Juicy turns to me and frowns.

Si laughs, picking up an Alaskan-Black-Ball-Breaker. He takes a large gulp. 'Baby Jesus! What's this?'

'Si, this is Juicy - I *mean* Lucy.'

'Hi,' Juicy smiles seductively.

'Oh ... hello there.'

I roll my eyes. 'He's my brother.'

'How sweet! Look, I hate to rush you, but do you want a lap dance? My boss keeps looking over.'

'Hang on a minute!' Si yells. 'Give the lad a chance, he's only just walked through the bleeding door.'

'Si, shut up!' I snap, raising a finger to my lips.

Tutting, Juicy spins around with a flick of her hair, and bumps into tables and chairs as she makes her way clumsily over to a group of businessmen on the far side of the room.

'What did you have to say that for, you prick? I was in there!'

'Look around you, Chris - there's hundreds of them! Let's get a table and have some fun - the first lap dance is on me!'

* * *

Chris is led away by a gorgeous blonde and I fear for his safety. Lucky bastard I think to myself, she's six-foot tall, slim and stunningly attractive. Scanning the room, I see the girl from earlier thrusting her butt cheeks in some sweaty guy's face, and reaching nervously for my drink I try to avoid eye contact with a toothy Thai girl dressed in red suspenders over in the corner. Having already spent a small fortune on the cover charge at twenty dollars a pop, I decide to be more selective.

'Hi, mind if I join you?' she asks.

'Sure, but I don't want a lap dance.'

She drops her smile. 'Why not?'

'Oh ... uh ... I'm out of cash,' I lie not wanting to hurt her feelings.

'No worry mister,' she grins before gliding on by.

Taking another gulp of whiskey I fidget uncomfortably in my chair.

'Hi there handsome.'

Looking up, I try and focus on a pair of black leather boots, and following them up to an impressive pair of thighs and past delightfully cut hot pants, I meet the smile of an angel somewhere above a perfectly flat midriff.

'Would you like a slammer?' she asks sweetly.

'Why the hell not,' I reply.

Removing a shot glass from a leather belt running across her shoulder she strides round to the front of my chair, straddles my lap and feeds me a shot of melon flavored vodka.

'What's your name handsome?'

'Simon,' I smile.

'I'm Eva. Where you from?'

'England.'

Her eyes light up. 'Wow. I'd love to go to England. I really fancy Prince William. Do you think he'd like me to pole dance for him?'

'*Yeah...*' I grin. 'I think he'd really appreciate that. You should go to England! But it's pretty cool here too!'

She shrugs. 'I guess so. I'm from LA originally.'

'Really? I'm heading that way tomorrow.'

'Say hi to the ol' place for me. How long you staying?'

'A couple of months.'

'You'll have a blast! Us California girls know how to have a good time. You single?' she asks, massaging my shoulders.

'Uh-huh, which is a good job considering where I am now.'

'You don't have to worry. What happens in Vegas...'

'...Stays in Vegas!' I grin.

'You got it babycakes,' she laughs. 'Travelling alone?'

I shake my head. 'No, with my brother ... and here he comes!'

Chris walks over hand-in-hand with his new friend

and with an enormous grin across his face.

'Can I get you another shot?' Eva asks, sliding her arm around my shoulder and looking suggestively into my eyes.

'Sure.'

She pours one into my mouth from the bottle, then turns to Chris and kicks her boots athletically at him. Politely paying his girl for the lap dance, we're left to kickback for a while and catch a bit of the show.

'Mate, get a private dance in - these girls are *not* shy!' he enthuses biting his lip as a petite, full-breasted beauty in a white cowboy hat kneels on a chair in front of us and spanks her bare bottom. 'I'm quite a broad-minded kind of a guy - but that's just *outrageous!*'

'She's mine,' I gasp, admiring the way she works the crowd.

The whole room seems to be drawn towards her. I can't quite put my finger on what makes her so incredibly desirable, apart from the obvious of course.

As she exits the stage the audience erupts in whistles and applause, and walking down the steps towards me, I catch her eye and surprise myself by gesturing for her to come over.

'Give me a minute,' she whispers, pressing a finger to my lips before disappearing into the crowd.

Speechless, I stare blankly into space.

'*YOU LUCKY BASTARD!*' Chris shouts, as he stumbles over his chair and makes a beeline for the bar.

I can feel my heart thumping in my chest at the prospect of her return, and my nervous fingers struggle to prise a cigarette from the crumpled packet. I suddenly feel the presence of someone crouching beside me and freeze.

'Did you want something?' A soft voice whispers in my ear.

Turning my head I'm absorbed by the green eyes of the

goddess.

'Will you dance for me?' I ask, feeling surprisingly comfortable with the question.

'Come with me.'

The room spins in slow motion as we weave through a maze of tables, and catching the jealous eyes of men all around me I feel privileged to be with her.

'Is this your first time?'

I nod as she directs me to a seat in the darkest corner of a room lined with couches - unsure if she means my first time in Vegas or my first lap dance.

Standing in front of me, she pauses for a moment to fix her hair and then to the sound of Dido she begins to slowly move her hips in time to the music. As I watch her undress she makes me feel totally at ease, as though we've known each other before, and reading my expression, she climbs across my lap and plays me like a musical instrument. She doesn't remove her tiny knickers, and lying with her head against my chest in a post-coital style embrace it feels strangely like we're in love.

'You're amazing,' I whisper.

'And you have the most hypnotic eyes. Can I dance for you again?'

Buying a few more minutes together, we talk for a while afterwards and I feel low as we return to my seat and part company. Ordering a large vodka and tonic, Chris explains how he also felt that Candy was interested in him, until he caught her all over some other guy.

'They're bloody lap dancers, for Christ's sake! What did we expect?'

I light another cigarette. 'I know, it's ridiculous. It's almost like we're pre-programmed to feel jealous, even though you know full well that you've just paid twenty dollars for the privilege of their attention. It just shows how powerful a woman can be - how easily they can manipulate you with a wink and a smile.'

Chris grins. 'Well, it was a bit more than a wink and smile.'

Some hours later, we stumble back out into the street hundreds of dollars lighter, but feeling incredibly inspired. The nightlife of Vegas calls, and as we take the opportunity to dance-till-dawn in a tacky venue that's gone for a beach theme, we cause trouble, win friends, lose strangers, get high, get caught and pass out.

California Screaming

Trapping your finger in a door, head-butting a low beam or biting your tongue is nothing compared to the excruciating pain I feel this morning. Reaching pathetically for a bottle of water, my head pounds my lungs scream for help and my stinging throat growls in anger. Blinking madly in an attempt to clear my blurred vision, I flick off the lid and down the entire bottle. Lying back in agony I decide to nurse my hangover and let Si drive for a change. Bright beams of light flash in front of my eyes, dancing erotically in time to the beat of the tyres rolling over the highway's cracked tarmac. My head knocks against the window and I sit up with a start.

'Si, are you OK?'

'Yeah. I'm fine. Bloody hell!' he laughs psychotically. 'You look like shit!'

'What do you expect. We didn't exactly stay in last night and have a quiet game of chess, did we?'

'Well if we did, it was the best game I've ever played.'

'Hang on!' I cry, urgently jabbing my fingers into my wallet. 'It's all coming back to me.'

'What is?'

'Last night. How much did we spend?'

Si shrugs. 'How much have we got left?'

I flash him the empty wallet.

'Well, we took eight hundred dollars out with us and we haven't got any of it left. *Excellent*!'

'What do you mean - that's shit loads!'

'Come on, Chris! Those girls were worth every fucking penny. 'I tell you I'm *loving* it! I haven't had this much fun in years.'

'You sure? Normally you fall into a dark depression after you've just been out on the raz.'

'Not this time, buddy-boy. I've been thinking a lot over the last few hours and I'm beginning to realise that our situation could actually be very beneficial to us both.'

'It's taken you this long to realise that?'

'Chris, don't take the piss. This journey hasn't been easy for me you know.'

'Yes it has. I'm the one who's done all the bloody driving.'

'No. Not in that way, you idiot. Look, I've had a lot on my plate recently.'

'Not anymore!'

'Yep. You're not wrong, mate.'

I place my hands together and smile. 'Oh, thank you Lord for inventing strip joints. In no time we'll be settled in LA and the world will be ours.'

Si hits the steering wheel with excitement. 'Great! Sounds like the bees-bollocks. I'd forgotten what fun it is to be a free agent.'

'That's right, my boy - a man of straw.'

'Well, you are now looking at the new me. From this point on I'm going to be as free as a pissing bird.'

'Very poetic, Si. Very poetic.'

* * *

I squint in the bright sunlight as we crawl towards a gas station near Barstow on Highway 15. Circling its peri meter I pull up alongside an over-flowing Dumpster that's nestling in a few feet of shade - the only shade for miles around. A large black raven swoops down from out of nowhere and hovers above our heads. Flapping its huge wings the bird eyes the van suspiciously before landing on top of a plastic bin bag melting in the heat of the day. With a loud squawk it tears it open, releasing the suffocating odour of decomposing banana skins and sour milk into the still air. We sit and watch as it buries its head inside and grabbing a half-eaten doughnut it flies off with its prize.

'I can't breath,' I utter weakly, resting my head on the steering wheel.

Beads of sweat cover Chris's face and his saturated swollen eyebrows glisten like two slimy black slugs per-ched above his eyes.

'I need a drink,' he groans, dabbing his forehead with the bottom of his T-shirt.

Falling from the van I head deliriously for the store. Inside I feel chilled to the bone as the air-con hits me like an arctic wind. Pulling at the door of a large fridge full of drinks I jerk backwards as I beat the magnetic force of the seal. Condensation instantly forms on the inside of the glass, and the icy chill of the freezer blows around my bare legs, making me suddenly conscious that I'm not wearing any boxer shorts.

I weakly stagger over to the till with a bottle of raspberry Snapple, and I'm surprised by a bald man wearing a thick roll-neck jumper and a shiny blue shell suit sunk into a foldaway chair that's squeezed between two aisles.

'Hot!' I smile.

Failing to get a response, I place my refreshments on the counter and turn my attention to the plump girl ope-rating the till. Her dark hair is swimming in grease, although she has softness that radiates behind her rosy cheeks.

'Do you want a straw, mister?

'No thanks.'

'We've got all kinds of colours, mister. What's your favourite colour?'

'Uh … blue.'

Crouching down behind the counter she pops up clutching a handful of straws.

'I'm sorry but we're clean out of blue. I only have yellow, red, purple and this orange one left.'

'It's not a problem.'

'They're only ten cents! Maybe you'd like a yellow one?' she beams, waving the straw in my face.

'No thanks.'

'A purple one?'

'It's fine! I *really* don't need a straw.'

'You sure?'

'*Yes*!'

'How about a red one?'

'OK! Go on, then. I'll take a red one,' I snap, fishing round in my pocket for some loose change.

Picking out the red straw she carefully balances it on top of the Snapple.

'Where you heading?'

'LA.'

'Have you just come from the ghost town?'

'No. Is there a ghost town round here?'

She enthusiastically nods. 'Yep. It's up at Calico, a few miles down. You should go. All the other tourists go.'

'It sounds interesting. Maybe next time.'

'Why don't you go *now*? It's only fifteen miles away.'

'It'll have to be another time, I'm afraid.'

'There might not be another time, mister,' she smiles, turning to the man in the deck chair. 'Isn't that right, Jimbo?'

The strange looking bald fella, whose tongue hangs lazily from his wet mouth, continues to stare vacantly in my direction.

I nod. 'I'm sure there will be.'

'But what if there isn't?'

'Well, maybe there won't be. Look, thanks for the straw but I'd better get going.'

'Done the lotto?' she suddenly cries, as I head for the exit.

I stop and turn back. 'The lotto?'

'Uh-huh … have you bought a lotto ticket?'

'No. I don't know anything about it.'

'How come? It's the $300,000,000 Powerball.'

I walk back to the counter.

'*How much*?'

'$300,000,000... that's a lotto money, don't you think?' she grins. 'You gotta get a ticket before seven tonight. Do you want one? You'll be missing out if you don't. Me and Jimbo got the winning numbers! Isn't that right, Jimbo?'

Jimbo doesn't reply. He just sits with his hands on his knees.

'I'm psychic, you see,' the girl mumbles, blowing a bubble with her gum. 'I've predicted all six winning numbers.'

'Really? Think how many blue straws you could buy if you win?'

She rolls back her eyes. 'I wouldn't buy blue straws, silly. Hell no. I'd buy a big yacht and a hundred mansions all looking out to sea. Isn't that right, Jimbo?'

'Cool,' I smile, turning to Jimbo.

'Don't mind him, mister. He's dumber than a mule.'

'Does he work here?'

'He's ma husband.'

'Oh … I'm sorry.'

She frowns. 'Bout what?'

'I'm sorry ... I didn't ... good luck with the lotto,' I wave, wiggling my fingers at Jimbo before returning to the fantastic heat outside.

* * *

Hurtling down the highway, Si pushes the van to its limits as we chase a mile-long freight train across the Mojave Desert.

'Whoooohooooo!' he cries, as we ride alongside the steel boxes that clank and rattle along the track.

The driver sounds his horn, so we toot ours and watch as the train accelerates away carriage by carriage over the horizon.

Reaching the outskirts of LA, we decide to avoid the chaos of the big city until morning and head further along the coast to the beach town of Oceanside. Driving for miles along winding roads, spots of rain suddenly appear on the window screen, and by the time we pull up at the seafront in a heavy shower I feel a sudden sadness. A familiar sadness, like when we were kids returning home from our camping holidays across Europe, back to reality and dark winter nights at the end of a long hot summer.

The next day I rise early and peer out across a wide expanse of sand; the tide is out and the sky overhead hangs low and grey. From the size of the puddles on the pavement it's been raining all night. I grab a newspaper from a nearby dispenser, whilst Si sits beneath an umbrella outside a marina café.

'What you sitting outside for?' I shiver, tossing the paper onto the table.

'I need some fresh air,' he replies, pouring sugar into

his cappuccino. 'I've got a headache.'

Si takes in a lung-full of clean air and looks round the marina. 'How the fuck did we get here?'

I shrug. 'I have *absolutely* no idea. It's bizarre to think that only yesterday we were in Vegas. Were we on a mission, or what? Look at the state of us!'

I sniff my armpit and screw up my face.

'Smell that!' I cry, pulling my T-shirt up to his nose.

'Fuck off, Chris! We need to sort ourselves out. I haven't changed my socks in days.'

'I know - isn't it great? Don't you feel so alive?'

Si peers up at the dark clouds. 'No.'

'You're right. I feel like shit, too. I think I've got piles.'

Spitting out his cappuccino, Si turns to me with a look of disgust. 'Don't be ridiculous!'

'*What*? I might have! I've definitely got athlete's foot. Look, if we're not careful we'll end up catching some itchy rash or insect borne disease. I'm telling you now, you don't want to know the weird shit you can catch on the road.'

'You're right ... I don't.'

'Take the Amazon for instance.'

'Chris! I don't want to know.'

'...In the Amazon you have to be careful when you go for a piss, because there's a creature called a catfish that swims up your urine stream and makes a home for itself up inside your bad boy.'

'Hmm ... thanks for that.'

'Just offering some friendly advice.'

'Well, apart from your piles we seem to have made it pretty intact, which is more than I can say for the van.'

'Hopefully we'll find somewhere to settle soon - you know, give the van a break for a while.'

'Uh-huh. Once we get to LA.'

'Hey ... talking of the van. Maybe we should give it a name?'

'A *name*? I'm not sure it deserves a name.'

'Why not?'

'It's been a fucking pain in the arse, if you ask me.'

'A pain in the arse? It's just carried us for thousands of miles. It's been a friend and companion.'

'It's a heap of junk.'

'You've changed your tune! What happened to all that bad karma bullshit?'

'It was bullshit.'

'Fair enough. What do you think to Rust Bucket Reg?'

Si shakes his head. 'That's shit!'

'Stan the Van?'

'Even shitter!'

'How about Hank? It looks a bit like a Hank, don't you think?'

'What, as in Hank the Tank?'

'*NO*! Just plain Hank.'

'That's *so* crap! Look you freak, forget about naming the van and concentrate on what's important – like, what we're going to do when we get to LA.'

'It's funny you mention that, because I haven't got a clue, either. Maybe we should head for the beach and become surf dudes?'

'Yeah. I guess so.'

'Jesus Christ, Si! Don't sound *too* enthusiastic!'

'Sorry. I think I'm a bit freaked out that we're nearly at LA.'

'What do you mean? We made it! Little you and me all the way from Seattle in an old banger.'

'I know! It's *crazy*! I just can't believe it's nearly over.'

'*Over*? What are you talking about? This is just the beginning. Before you know it we'll be in the company of two beautiful bikini babes, drinking cocktails and wishing our visas would never expire.'

'I just hope the weather clears up. Its August for fuck's sake - it should be sunny!'

'Don't worry. It'll pass. In fact, what are we waiting for? Let's get moving.'

'What's the rush? Give me a minute to finish my coffee and read my stars and I'll be right with you.'

I peer down at the newspaper. 'You don't believe in all of that horoscope bullshit, do you?'

'Of course I don't. I just like to read them,' Si mutters, scanning the page for Scorpio.

'It's bollocks! The people who get paid to write that crap aren't from this planet you know. If you ask me, I think they should all be rounded up, bundled into a rocket and fired into outer space. Especially that Russell Grant dude.'

'You're entitled to your opinion, although, if you shut your mouth for a second and listen to what Mystic Mike has to say, you might learn something interesting about your future.'

I straighten my posture and clear my throat.

'Mobilise all your reserves of courage, foresight and fortitude to embrace conclusive developments in your key relationships. The impulse to commit, separate or restructure becomes a concrete reality and adjusting to the new order could prove challenging. Focus on your talent for personal transformation and release the past.'

Si looks up with a smile. 'What do you think?'

'Utter rubbish.'

'I thought it was quite relevant. Release the past - move forwards.'

'But that could relate to anybody?'

Si tosses the paper across the table and rubs his eyes. 'I'd like to see you do better.'

'All right, then: A positive and enlightening few months lay ahead ... so ... uh ... move your ass and make your way towards the golden sands, where the position of the sun will bring joy and an overwhelming desire to get laid!'

'Actually, Chris! That was surprisingly good.'

'You think so?'

'Yeah. But I wouldn't give up your day job.'

'I haven't got a day job.'

* * *

Paying for our coffees, I trail behind Chris down to the quayside. We watch the small sailboats bob up and down in the marina for a while, and spotting the Sea Front Internet Café squeezed between Dino's Surf Store and Oceanside Flowers, we decide to check our email and let everyone know where we are. I haven't checked my email since England and I begin to feel butterflies in my stomach as we make our way inside. It's weird because I've become so involved in the journey that I haven't really thought about what might be happening back home. I'm suddenly very curious to find out.

Sitting on a swivel chair in front of the flickering screen, I'm immediately reminded of work and instinctively seize the mouse as if it were an extension of my hand. Logging onto Hotmail I bite my nails as the hour glass icon hangs for what feels like an eternity, and I try to control my breathing as the computer loads my inbox and I scan the list of emails. Considering I haven't checked my account for three weeks, I feel disappointed to find only fifteen new messages. Going down the list, I skip past the porn and spam to see four messages, one from our dad, one from my good friend Dermot, one from our older brother and one from Emily... *EMILY*? Fuck! The words Emily Willow twist in my gut. Grabbing a cigarette I place it shakily between my lips and hastily light up.

'Excuse me, sir,' the young lad on the front desk calls

from across the café. 'You can't smoke in here.'

I stub out the cigarette on the packet and drop my head.

'What's the matter?' Chris asks, leaning over to look at my screen.

'Oh … nothing.'

The title of the email is blank and I pause for a second with fear of what might be inside. Come on, you pussy. Clicking on her name the screen reloads before I've had time to change my mind and the message flicks up. I check the date and it's nearly two weeks old. Questions jump around inside my head. Why has she emailed me now? What can there possibly be left to say? Has something happened to her? Has she met someone else?

"Hi, honey!
What the hell are you doing in America? I was trying to call your mobile all week, but I bumped into Dermot in Camden and he told me you'd gone travelling with Chris. I think that's great - I'm really happy for you. Things have been going OK for me – works been stressful and my mum's been driving me CRAZY, but apart from that everything's fine. I know this may seem odd after all the stuff that's happened to us lately, but I really need to see you Raven … I miss you babes. Call me on my mobile when you get back and maybe we could meet for a drink? Only if you want to of course. Take care, baby.
Luv Em xx"

Feeling sick I look over at Chris who's typing urgently. He looks up from his keyboard and grins, before turning his attention back to the probable filth he's writing. Clicking the back button, I return to my inbox and open the email from my college buddy Dermot.

"Hey, Mother fucker! Suck my big hairy balls!

You fucker's must be somewhere deep in the ass of the U.S of A. by now - give her one for me. You're missing absolutely fuck-all here so don't rush home. I saw that slut of yours in Caaaamden (innit). She asked about you. She was looking pretty fine - you idiot!!!!!
Anyway dude, I'm gonna love ya leave ya nutta. Slap your fool brother for me.

DD

Ps ... SUCK IT!!"

With a smile, I reply with a simple *"FUCK YOU"*, as Dermot would expect, and distract myself for a while by replying to my dad and brother, who cheer me up with tales of comedy disaster in the Raven family. Sitting back for a second I stare out of the window and watch a little dog cock its leg and pee against the wheel of a baby's pram. I realise that for the first time since I left England I feel home sick, and picturing my mum pottering around in the garden or having beers down the pub with our dad and brother, I wish I could pop home and see them all.

Re-reading Emily's email half a dozen times I log off and make my escape. Chris is still heavily involved in his replies, so I go in search of air and find a comfortable spot on the steps outside. Looking out across the ocean I can see the cloud starting to lift and the sun working hard to shine through. Going over Emily's words in my head I try to analyse how I feel. The last thing I had expected was to hear from her again. She is dead as far as I'm concerned. I spent the past few months in London grieving for her and to suddenly hear her voice again has sent a deep shiver down my spine. It seems ironic that after the great distances we've covered in the van, the lifetime we have lived over the past few weeks on the road, I arrive at our destination to find her at the end of it all. I feel deeply disturbed by the idea of seeing her again, that ten thousand miles away, the girl who broke my heart was asking to see me.

Chris budges up on the step next to me and I turn to him with glazed eyes.

'Did you reply to dad's email?' he chuckles. 'Funny fucker!'

'Oh ... yeah.'

'What's up with you? You look a bit pale ... well, paler than usual.'

'Emily sent me an email,' I reply, as calmly as possible.

'Emily? As in Emily Willow?'

'Yes! Emily, you prick!'

'No frigging way! What did she say?'

'She wants to see me.'

'Is that what she said?'

'Uh-huh.'

'Fuck that for a game of soldiers, right?'

I look away.

'You're not thinking of actually meeting her, are you?'

'*No*! Oh ... I don't know. What do you think?'

'Si, she fucking dumped you! She's fucking with your head - it's the oldest trick in the book, for shit's sake.'

'Yeah - you're *right*.'

'How do you feel about it?'

I shrug. 'I don't know. She said she misses me.'

'The best thing you could do ... the best thing you have done ... is to move on. It's like you said, if you had to choose now between Tiffany and Emily you'd choose Tiffany.'

'Did I say that?'

'To me that says it all.'

'Yeah, but would it hurt to just meet up with her?'

'I'm not convinced you could handle it. I would never put you off if that's what you want but be careful, mate.

175

Your relationship only ended a few months ago.'

'I'm over her, Chris. Although, I think I'd like to see her when we get back. You know, finally lay her to rest and all that?'

'Just don't lay her.'

'Shut up! I want her to see that I've moved on. What's wrong with that? Would you meet up with Chloe if she emailed you?'

'No.'

'Why not?'

'Why would I?'

'To say hello, maybe...'

Chris raises his hand. 'Uh ... to say "hello"? Fuck that! I haven't seen Chloe for a while now. It was fun while it lasted, but meeting up for casual sex just isn't good for your mind. I've moved on like *you* have. Actually, Si. Come to think of it, I'm talking out of my arse. Maybe you should meet up with her. It might do you some good.'

'You think?'

Chris stands up. 'Yeah. Confront your demons. Sometimes it's the only way to move on.'

During the majority of years I spent working, I managed to justify the monotony of my job through my relationship. Work was a means to an end and the most important aspect of my life was Emily - everything else had to revolve around her. When our relationship ended, I was left feeling unchallenged and alone, and looking back I see I had made the classic mistake of using the security of a relationship to distract me from making hard decisions about my future. I had ignored the most important ingredient necessary for a happy human - pursuing my passions, and ironically it was my depression from not doing just that, that had torn our relationship apart.

For many of us the very idea of "giving it all up" to go

in search of something unspecific, isn't an option. Despite any dissatisfaction we feel with our lives, the most important thing to hold onto is security and continuity: of friends, of family, of work, of money and possessions, of status and lifestyle.

The Shitty Shoes Blues

'I'm going to seriously road rage the next bastard that beeps their horn up my fucking arse!' Si yells, thrusting his middle finger out the window at the car behind.

This isn't a good idea, particularly in a country famous for drive-by shootings and serial killers, but the look on his face tells me not to argue with him on this one. The volume of traffic on the roads has increased dramatically since our arrival in California, and as we struggle to keep up with the minimum speed limit of 45mph, especially uphill, we often become the cause of a long tailback.

Much to our relief we finally reach the outskirts of LA, swerve off the hellish six-lane highway and head for the coast. Palm trees and pretty girls line the streets, as we cruise down quieter roads and snake through wealthy suburbs until we see signs for Venice Beach. Astonished by the level of activity outside our window, we watch in awe as the hungry Pacific swallows up surfers and spits them out across the shoreline. Beautiful women accompanied by muscular men parade along the beachfront like models on a catwalk, and a freaky Jimi Hendrix lookalike roller-skates past zigzagging through the crowds whilst strumming an electric guitar.

Locking up we walk purposefully along the beachfront roadway, jostling through sun-tanned crowds towards a row of tacky seaside shops further along the promenade.

Buying a couple of cheeky postcards of Californian girls in various poses I fish around for some cash, but realise I've left my wallet in the van.

'Bollocks! I've forgot my money.'

'That was clever,' Si mocks. 'You'll just have to go back and get it.'

'Can't you lend me some?'

'Nooo fucking way, pal, I'm not lending you jack shit!'

'Why not?'

'Hmm...' Si replies, tapping his chin. 'Ah, I know! Because you *never* pay me back!'

'That's rubbish! I hate people who never pay money back. I'm paranoid about paying people back.'

'I don't care!'

'This is ridiculous! I'm your twin brother, for Christ's sake. We're talking about five fucking dollars.'

Tutting, Si jabs his fingers into his pocket. 'OK you little tosser, but there's a dollar interest for each day you forget to pay me back ... all right?'

'Fine.'

He starts to search more thoroughly through other pockets, ramming his hands into his tight jeans. 'Uh ... it seems I've also left my wallet. We'll have to go back to the van.'

Like two smelly fugitives on the run, we tear along the promenade to find a man in uniform stood by the van.

'Hey ... excuse me,' Si grovels, sliding up beside the large gentleman. 'We've literally been away for two minutes. We didn't realise we had to buy a ticket. If we put some money in the meter now everything will be cool, right?'

The traffic warden looks up from his pad for a nanosecond and then returns to his work.

'Please! We seriously didn't know. We were so excited about arriving in LA. We're from England. This is our first time in America.'

He doesn't look too impressed that it's our first time in America. We could have just donated two kidneys to save the life of the President and the First Lady and he still wouldn't give a damn. With a shake of the head he starts circling the van to take down our particulars.

'Oh, come on!' Si starts shouting. 'You can't do this to us. We're *tourists*!'

The traffic warden stops what he is doing, considers saying something, but thankfully through heavy eyelids simply throws us a withering look before writing the ticket and slapping it on the windshield. End of story.

Giving us a 'Have a nice day - hope you don't slip and die,' smirk, he wobbles off, his fat ass swaggering somewhere behind him John Wayne style.

'*WHAT A WANKER*!' Si yells, whipping the piece of paper from beneath the wiper.

'How much is it?' I ask.

'You're not going to believe this!'

'Try me.'

'*SIXTY FUCKING DOLLARS*!'

'*FUCK*! We should've checked first!' I groan. 'Why didn't we check first?'

'Oh … bollocks to it, Chris. I refuse to get angry.'

'I can't believe we've driven four thousand miles without getting a fine and then … *BOOM*!'

'Look, it's only thirty dollars each.'

'What do you mean "*only*"? That's one and a half lap dances thank you very much.'

Si clicks his fingers. 'Wait a minute! Hold the fucking phones! What are we getting all worked up for? Let's not pay!'

'We'll get into trouble.'

'No we won't! Think about it dumb-ass. We don't live in this country. We don't have an address. How are they *ever* going to track us down?'

'But we gave that mechanic bloke in Seattle our address.'

'No. We were meant to phone him and give him an address so he could send us the logbook. And did we?'

'Like fuck we did. Well done Si, you've just saved me thirty dollars!'

Snatching the ticket out of his hand, I tear the fine in two and toss the pieces into the air.

'Let's get some pancakes!'

'Apart from the pancakes, Crissy-boy. I couldn't agree more.'

* * *

Chris watches in amusement as I skid in a huge pile of dog shit.

'FUCK!' I cry, hopping manically on one foot. 'Bastard dogs! Why can't people clean up after their canines?'

'Keep your hair on!'

'Piss off! The stuff stinks ... look!' I shout, removing my trainer.

'Yeah, OK, very nice, Si. Come on, let's check this place out.'

After stopping to admire an extremely pale skinny man wearing colourful parrot boxer shorts, who manages to contort his body through a stringless tennis racket, we hang a sharp right down a pedestrian avenue. We pass lots of expensive looking restaurants, and feeling my stomach growl I suggest we grab a bite to eat in a pleasant looking place called Rococo.

Squeezing between tables of sharp looking guys and immaculately groomed women, we find a nice spot on the veranda and wait to be served.

'It's a bit posh here, ain't it?' Chris whispers, sneaking

glances around the restaurant.

'Yeah,' I grin, flicking through the menu. 'What you going to have?'

'I don't know. It all looks delicious. How about the herb-roasted salmon mayonnaise with peppered cucumber and a side of fries?'

'Hold your bleeding horses! How much does that little number cost?'

'Twenty dollars.'

'*What*? Fuck that, Chris. I'm not paying twenty dollars for fish 'n' chips. I'll have a bowl of soup and a coke.'

'A bowl of soup and a coke? You are joking?'

'We can't afford these prices. Unless you've suddenly won the -'

'Hey … can you smell something?'

'No,' I reply, sniffing the air.

'You sure?'

'*Yes*!' I snap, feeling suddenly paranoid.

Wafting up the air from beneath the table Chris freezes in horror. 'You're not going to believe this.'

'What?'

'I think I can smell shit!'

'No you can't?'

'I fucking can! When was the last time you changed your pants?'

'About two days ago - *hey*! It's not me that smells of shit!'

'Well, it's not me! Maybe it's that dog shit on your trainers?'

'It *can't* be! I wiped it off.'

Chris grabs my foot and pulls it up to his nose.

'Fucking hell!' he coughs, screwing up his face. 'It is you! It's all stuck in the grooves!'

'That's disgusting! Should we leave?'

'Too late. Here comes the waiter.'

Observing the scowling face of the smartly dressed

gentleman approaching us, we fidget uncomfortably in our seats.

'Sorry, guys. This table is reserved,' he snootily informs us, glancing down at our bare legs.

'Not a problem.' Chris lifts himself out of his chair. 'We were just leaving.'

'Wait a sec!' I cry, turning to the waiter. 'Where do you want us to move to?'

'Unfortunately, the restaurant is full today, sir, and also we have a no shorts policy here at Rococo.'

'Oh, *really*! So, what exactly are you trying to say exactly?'

'Forget it, Si. People are looking at us.'

'They can't do this! We're the customer and the customer is always right.'

'Let's just go somewhere else. Somewhere less up it's own arse.'

We grab our scruffy bags off the floor and head for the exit - leaving our pride behind and the faint odour of dog shit hanging in the air.

'*I WOULDN'T EAT HERE ANYWAY*!' I yell over my shoulder, as we stumble out onto the street. '*WHO THE FUCK DO THEY THINK THEY ARE?*'

'Si, calm down! We obviously don't look cool enough.'

'Cool enough? What are you talking about? This T-shirt is top dollar. I've lived in London, for fuck's sake - *I KNOW THE SCORE*!'

Making our way back towards the seafront, we sulk on the promenade with a bag of greasy chips from a burger van in a sad attempt to cheer ourselves up.

'Si, maybe we need to make more of an effort now that we're back in the city.'

'What do you mean?'

'You know. Get some nice clothes. Buy a pair of shoes.'

'*Fuck off*! I didn't come all this way to spend my

money on new shoes.'

'Well, if we plan to stick around LA we'll have to try and fit in.'

'Chris, I thought we came on this trip to travel and see the world, not to fall back into all that pretentious city crap?'

'You're right! What the fuck am I talking about?'

'I know! "*Buy some shoes*"? You're having a laugh!'

Being in LA reminds me of everything I had grown to hate about London: its rules, regulations and crowds of wannabes congesting the restaurants, bars and pavements. Life was exciting when I first arrived in London – no commitments, a poor student living in the shadow of a cool underground scene. London was one big playground of adventure, but all that changed when I joined the rat race. I started to drink in fashionable bars instead of creating my own. I'd buy designer T-shirts, instead of wearing second-hand clothes from Oxfam. I guess its normal to aspire to something better as you get older, but I can't help thinking that I sold out before really understanding that there are a number of ways to lead a better life.

Mexico

Si parks the van carelessly on a double yellow line opposite a Denny's Diner. Standing on the sidewalk we wait to cross the busy road. The minutes zoom by and so does the traffic as we watch the little restaurant flash behind the cars, motorbikes and buses that roar past at speed. People in their vehicles stare at us open mouthed, as if we're stood stark naked holding a sign which reads 'Ban Burgers and Coffee', and apart from an old tramp scratching his bollocks close by, we seem to be the only people walking the streets.

'Sod this, Chris. We're going to be here all day.'

'Come on, mate. It's only a few yards away. I'm not letting a fucking road get in the way of me and my pancakes.'

We finally make it across and nab a table by the window. Endless cups of coffee later, we come to the conclusion that staying in LA for any length of time is simply out of the question.

'I mean, I'm sure it'd be a great place to live if you worked in film or TV and enjoyed playing the game, drinking the drinks, living the bullshit.'

'Yeah. I don't know what we thought we'd find down here,' Si replies. 'Maybe a kind of Val Kilmer in *The Doors* type thing - sleeping on the beach and strumming a guitar on Tricks rooftop.'

'You cheesy bastard,' I mumble, cream and syrup squirting out of my pancake.

'Bloody hell, Chris! Don't you ever stop eating?'

'Are you calling me a fat bastard?'

Si shakes his head. 'No, but at the rate you're going you will be.'

'Piss off! I'm a grown man. Food is energy.'

'Whatever, fat boy. I know we've only just arrived, but maybe we should consider leaving?'

'Give us a chance! I haven't finished my other pancake yet.'

'*No*! Leave LA, you idiot. Can you honestly imagine sleeping in the van around here?'

'But we've come so far. We can't *just* leave! Maybe we could drive out of town and park up along the coast?'

'We'd get bored. It's not like anybody else is living like this. Besides, we're skint. How can you enjoy the buzz of a city if you've got no money?'

'We should have thought about this. Hey! What about finding some cash-in-hand work for a few weeks?'

'Fuck that!'

'Why not? It might be a good laugh.'

'Chris, I've spent the last four years of my life working. It wasn't a good laugh. I just want to find somewhere to chill for a while. Anyway, I thought the idea of this trip was to buy us some thinking time - not to spend all day flipping greasy burgers.'

'OK. Let's head back on the road.'

Si rests his head in his hand and looks out of the window. 'The van's a bit of a worry, though.'

'Jesus Christ!'

'What?'

'Make up your frigging mind. Do we stay or do we go?'

Si leans back and takes a sip of his coffee. 'Look, basically, if we stay here we'll have a nightmare with the parking inspectors, and if we carry on we'll end up breaking down in the desert.'

'Hmm ... OK. So, spend the rest of your life in jail for

killing a LA traffic warden, or have the vultures peck your eyes out in the desert. I think I'd rather risk dying in the desert.'

'Then it's agreed!' Si grins. 'Let's keep on driving until the wheels fall off.'

'Sounds perfecto.'

Si signals to our haggard-looking waitress and she charges across the restaurant with a hot pot of coffee.

'You guys wanna refill?'

'Yes please, and the check.'

'No problem.'

She pours and then pulls a notepad from out of her frilly pinny, tearing off the top sheet and placing it between us on the table.

'That'll be nine-fifty,' she rasps in a hard New York Italian accent.

'Are you from around here?' Si asks, trying to charm her with his winning smile.

'For the past thirty years,' she chuckles. 'But I'll always be a Brooklyn girl at heart. You guys English?'

'Yes,' we chime in unison.

'You don't look English, and I mean that in a good way. How long you been in LA?'

'We just arrived,' I chip in. 'But I think we're leaving today.'

'We're not quite ready for LA, yet,' Si grins.

'Took me about fifteen years so I wouldn't be too hard on yourselves. The weather kind of grows on you, but the people don't so much.'

Si picks up his coffee cup. 'We've just driven from Seattle in a van.'

'Seattle you say. Hmm … they do good coffee in Seattle. Well, if you like driving then you've come to the right place.'

'We're not enjoying this kind of driving. The van we bought is fading fast.'

'Without wheels in this town you're kind of screwed, boys. Only Mexicans on the buses.'

'Hey!' calls a voice from behind the counter, and a fat Mexican guy looks up from his grill. 'You keep me out of this!'

'Get back to work you illegal alien!' she ribs, chuckling again.

'Hey, lady! Don't even joke about that. I could spend a life in jail for that kind of fun. I sung the *Spangley Banner* in Pomona like the best American.'

She swings back to us and sighs. 'All Mexicans are so paranoid.'

'I'd love to go to Mexico,' I call to him. 'It's meant to be beautiful.'

'You said it, man,' he shouts back. 'The best country in the world. Our beaches make California look like a sand pit!'

We settle up and go, leaving them to carry on sparring their way through the morning. But it does get us thinking.

'We can't drive in Mexico, Si - it'd be suicide!' I mutter, climbing into the driver's seat.

'Who said anything about taking the van?'

'What? Get rid of Hank?'

'He'd only weigh us down.'

'No he wouldn't. He may be a bit slow, but he's got *miles* left in him yet.'

'Do you really think so?'

'Of course I do. He's just a bit shit in city traffic. Let's drive to Florida instead.'

'*Florida*?'

I nod. 'Uh-huh. Come on! It'll be great!'

'You do realise where Florida is in relation to LA?'

'It's on the East Coast.'

'Thousands of miles away! The van's days are numbered, Chris. It's on its last legs. We can't survive in

America without wheels.'

'Yeah, but a few months ago in Brighton I met this girl from Daytona Beach. She could show us around. It's supposed to be a great place ... Hey! She may even have a pretty friend.'

'Really? Have you got her number?'

'Uh-huh ... although, maybe it is too far.'

'Make up your bloody mind.'

'Well, I've just remembered something.'

'What?'

'She had hairy armpits!'

Si screws up his face. 'Yuck.'

'I know. I know. I've still got this terrifying image of her lying naked on my bed, with her arms up behind her head, and two overgrown hedges protruding from her pits.'

'I'll bet that messed up your concentration a bit.'

'You're telling me! I didn't have the heart to tell her I found it *really* disturbing.'

'So did you, or didn't you?'

'Of course I did. Hey, can't we just get Hank fixed?' I cry, quickly changing the subject.

'It's too late for that. If the transmission was damaged way back in Riggins, imagine how bad it must be now?'

'Well, let's trade it in and get something smaller?'

'We won't get anything for it - a hundred dollars for scrap if we're lucky.'

'Shit.'

'Look, Chris. Let's just cut our losses and head for Mexico. We could buy hammocks, stay in beach cabanas, learn Spanish and drink shit loads of tequila! The border's only a few hours down the road and we can ditch the van there.'

'We can't just abandon poor Hank in a car park,' I wail, getting emotional all over again.

'Well, there's no way I'm spending hours driving round

scrap yards for a hundred dollars.'

'Aren't you even a little bit gutted that we'd lose the van, Si? It would be the end of the road ... no more freedom of the highway ... no more tinned meatball sandwiches.'

He narrows his eyes. 'Of course I'm gutted, but maybe it's time to move on. Just imagine all of those lovely Latino ladies waiting for us to rock into town and show them a good time.'

'Do you think so?'

'No, Chris. I fucking know so!'

* * *

The engine grinds in pain. Chris refuses to give up and presses hard on the gas. Suddenly, Hank jumps into life and revving uncontrollably, we waste no time in dragging the old heap back out onto the highway.

'Are you sure this is a good idea, Si?'

I give a reassuring nod. 'I've never felt more certain about anything in my entire life.'

'Mexico? We never planned to go to *Mexico*!'

'Plans change, fat boy. Fuck LA! Fuck London! Let's see what lies over the next horizon.'

Our top speed drops to a tragic 35mph, the worst it has ever been. Thick black smoke billows out of the exhaust, and cars and juggernauts fill the rear view mirror, all beeping their horns as they swerve to avoid us.

'This is dangerous!' Chris yells. 'We're not going fast enough!'

'Tell somebody who gives a shit!' I psychotically grin.

'This is going to take us till midnight.'

'I don't care if it takes till Christmas! We started our

journey in this van and we're going to finish our journey in this van.'

'But it's so *hot*! We should pull over for a few minutes and let the engine cool down?'

I shake my head. 'No way! If we stop now, we'll *never* get it started again. Let's keep on going, Crissy boy – let's keep old Hank alive!'

After four hours of solid driving, and after battling against the intense heat of the engine and a torrent of abuse from our fellow road users, we reach the Mexican border. Pulling up in a one-hour parking zone Chris cuts the engine, and with a final rattle and splutter Hank falls silent for the last time. I place a hand on the dashboard, pausing for a moment out of respect.

'It's over, Chris. He's dead. If it makes you feel any better I'm sure he's gone to that big scrap yard in the sky.'

We both look heavenwards and smile.

'At least the last few weeks of his life were exciting,' Chris nods. 'He left this world a happy van.'

Leaving the keys in the ignition we gently close the doors behind us, and lifting our rucksacks onto our shoulders in silence we glance back at Hank one last time.

'I wonder what will happen to him, Si? I mean, where will he end up?'

'I guess that's something we'll never know. One thing's for sure, I certainly won't forget him in a hurry.'

'No. Nor will I, mate. Nor will I.'

An overwhelming sensation of freedom washes over me, as we stride out across the car park towards a footbridge that arches like a rainbow into Mexico. A heavily moustached customs officer greets us on the other side and thumps a stamp in our passports before waving us through. Exiting the immigration building we're thrown into the chaos of Tijuana, and feeling a little paranoid we find a bank, change a pile of travellers cheques into pesos and somehow make it to the long distance bus station without being robbed. Purchasing two tickets bound for Mexico City we toss our belongings into the open luggage compartment of a tired looking bus, and greeting the pop-bellied driver with a nervous grin, feel like little boys in our shorts as we try to ignore the curious eyes of our fellow passengers.

'Hey! What's Spanish for beautiful?' Chris grins, as we squeeze down the aisle.

I shake my head. 'I don't know. Maybe we should buy a phrase book?'

'Good idea! But what's Spanish for phrase book?'

From one insane world to another I think to myself as we rattle along potholed streets and dusty threadbare suburbs.

Deep in thought Chris stares into space.

'Are you OK?'

He turns to me and nods. 'Yeah. I'm fine.'

'What you thinking about?'

'Nothing, really. I was just trying to imagine what a *bus* would look like if you took out all the seats. It'd be *huge* wouldn't it?'

Everything before now is a blur.

THE END

COMING SOON FROM SAMOSIR BOOKS

Living the Linger Longer (UK to Vladivostok)

SIMON RAVEN   CHRIS RAVEN

With a squeaky foot pump and an SAS survival guide, Simon Raven and Chris Raven drive in a £300 Ford Sierra from the East Midlands to the Far Eastern City of Vladivostok in Siberia.

Tales of their 11,000 mile adventure, which took them half-way around the world, will be published soon in their second book Living the Linger Longer.

Order your copy of Living the Linger and Living the Linger Longer online at:

www.samosirbooks.com

Email the authors:
chris.raven@samosirbooks.com
simon.raven@samosirbooks.com